Intermediate Mathematics C
Student Guide

Illustrations Credits

All illustrations © K12 Inc. unless otherwise noted

About K12 Inc.

K12 Inc., a technology-based education company, is the nation's leading provider of proprietary curriculum and online education programs to students in grades K–12. K¹² provides its curriculum and academic services to online schools, traditional classrooms, blended school programs, and directly to families. K12 Inc. also operates the K¹² International Academy, an accredited, diploma-granting online private school serving students worldwide. K¹²'s mission is to provide any child the curriculum and tools to maximize success in life, regardless of geographic, financial, or demographic circumstances. K12 Inc. is accredited by CITA. More information can be found at www.K12.com.

ISBN: 978-1-60153-483-5

Printed by Courier, Kendallville, IN, USA, May 2015, Lot 052015

Table of Contents

Slope and Proportional Thinking

Lines

Systems of Equations

Function Basics

Semester Review and Test

Linear Models

Basic Geometric Shapes

Volume

Transformations, Congruence, and Similarity

Irrational Numbers

The Pythagorean Theorem

End-of-Year Project

Semester Review and Test

Student Guide
Lesson 1: Semester 1 Introduction

Welcome to Intermediate Math C. In this course, you will continue to lay the groundwork for more advanced mathematics courses, especially algebra.

In this unit, you'll learn about number properties, including the order of operations and properties of positive and negative exponents. Then you will use scientific notation and orders of magnitude to make sense of very big and very small numbers.

PREPARE

Approximate lesson time is 60 minutes.

Advance Preparation

- You may download the Student Guide and Learning Coach Guide for the entire unit from the Materials tab in the first lesson. Lesson-level guides are available in each lesson.

Materials

For the Student

Intermediate Mathematics C: A Reference Guide and Problem Sets

LEARN
Activity 1: Semester Introduction *(Online)*

Activity 2: Digital Materials *(Online)*

This activity explains how to use the K12 Online Book. It also explains where you can download PDFs of the Online Book and the Student Guide.

Student Guide

Expressions

Think about the steps you take to brush your teeth. First, you pick up a toothbrush. Then you put toothpaste on the toothbrush and brush your teeth. When you're done, you put the toothbrush away and rinse. Could you change that order? Suppose you decide to put toothpaste on the toothbrush after you've brushed your teeth. Would that make sense? Sometimes order matters, and in this lesson you will see how grouping symbols indicate the exact order to follow so that you simplify an expression correctly.

Goals for the Lesson

- Simplify a numerical expression without grouping symbols.
- Simplify a numerical expression with grouping symbols.
- Place grouping symbols in an expression to create a specific value.

Graded Activities in This Lesson
Lesson Quiz (computer-scored)

Materials
Intermediate Mathematics C: A Reference Guide and Problem Sets, pages 7–10

Optional
Calculator

Keywords

grouping symbols: devices, such as parentheses, brackets, and fraction bars, used to set apart an expression that should be simplified before other operations are performed
order of operations: the order in which operations must be computed when more than one operation is involved

Groundwork: Preparing for the Lesson [online]
You will simplify some expressions to see what you already know about the order of operations. You will also review powers.

Learn: What a Group! [online]
You will learn how to use the order of operations to simplify expressions that either contain or do not contain grouping symbols.

Summarize what you learned in this activity.

1. If you are simplifying an expression, in what order should operations be performed if there are no grouping symbols?

2. Simplify. $24 + 18 \div 9 \cdot 3 - 14$

3. When a numerical expression contains parentheses, in what order should you perform the operations?

4. Simplify. $3^2 + 4(7 + 2)$

5. When a numerical expression contains grouping symbols within grouping symbols, in what order should you perform operations?

6. Simplify. $40 \div [6 + 2(5 - 3)]$

7. How do you simplify an expression that contains a fraction bar?

8. Simplify. $\dfrac{20 + 2(3 + 5)}{16 - 49 \div 7}$

Worked Examples: Expressions [online]

Use the space below to work through the examples you see in the online screens.

Summary: Expressions [online]

When simplifying expressions, you must follow the order of operations.

- Evaluate grouping symbols from the "inside out."
- Work through the top and bottom of a fraction (the numerator and denominator) as if the parts are in parentheses.
- Calculate powers.
- Multiply and divide from left to right.
- Add and subtract from left to right.

Offline Learning: Expressions [offline]

Read pages 7–9 in the Reference Guide.

Problem Sets

Complete Problems 1–17 odd and 26–28 on pages 9–10.

Extra Practice (optional)
Complete Problems 2–24 even on pages 9–10 for extra practice (optional).

Challenge (optional)
For a challenge, complete Problems 31 and 32 on page 10 (optional).

Lesson Assessment: Expressions Quiz [online]

Now go back online to complete the lesson quiz.

Student Guide

The Distributive Property

Using the distributive property is a lot like deciding how to schedule playing time for some 5-year-old soccer players. They're all excited about playing, but you need to distribute the time so every child plays an equal amount of time during the game. Likewise, when you distribute in mathematics, you will see a group of terms inside parentheses multiplied by a number outside the parentheses. Whether there are two, three, four, or more terms, you must make sure every term inside the parentheses gets multiplied.

Goals for This Lesson

- Simplify an expression using the distributive property.

- Identify like terms.

- Collect like terms.

Graded Activities in This Lesson
Lesson Assessment (computer-scored)

Materials
Intermediate Mathematics C: A Reference Guide and Problem Sets, pages 11–14

Keywords
simplifying an expression: replacing an expression with an equivalent expression that has as few terms as possible

like terms: terms with the same variable and the same exponent

common factor: a factor that is the same for two or more integers or terms

Skills Update: Practice Your Math Skills [online]
Complete the Skills Update online.

Groundwork: Preparing for the Lesson [online]
You will review the order of operations in order to prepare for simplifying more complex expressions later in the lesson.

Learn: Distribute Equally [online]

You will learn about the very important and widely used distributive property.

Summarize what you learned in this activity.

1. Explain the distributive property over addition or subtraction in your own words.

2. Expain the symmetric property..

Worked Examples: Try Distributing Equally [online]

Use the space below to work through the examples you see in the online screens.

Learn: Combining Like Terms [online]

You will learn about the very important and widely used distributive property.

Summarize what you learned in this activity.

1. How do you add like terms?

2. How do you subtract like terms?

3. If a company charges one price for the first hour and a different price per hour for each additional hour, what expression represents the number of additional hours if the total number of hours is *h*?

MathCast: Combining Like Terms [online]
View the video to see how to solve a typical problem.

Worked Examples: Try Combining Like Terms [online]
Use the space below to work through the examples you see in the online screens.

Summary: The Distributive Property [online]

The distributive property of multiplication over addition states that instead of simplifying what is in parentheses first, you may choose to multiply each term by the factor outside the parentheses.

$$a(b + c) = ab + ac$$

The distributive property of multiplication over subtraction also states that instead of doing what is in parentheses first, you may choose to multiply each term by the factor outside the parentheses.

$$a(b - c) = ab - ac$$

Like terms are terms that are constants, or they are terms that have a common variable factor whose exponents are identical.

When combining like terms that involve variables, only add or subtract the coefficients. The exponents of the variables remain the same.

Offline Learning: The Distributive Property [offline]

Read pages 11–13 in the Reference Guide.

Problem Sets

Complete Problems 1–15 odd and 17–23 all on page 14.

Extra Practice (optional)

Complete Problem 28 on page 14 for extra practice (optional).

Lesson Assessment: The Distributive Property Quiz [online]

Now go back online to complete the lesson quiz.

Student Guide

Positive Exponents

A shortcut is a way to do something more quickly and often more easily than the way it is usually done. Mathematics is full of shortcuts. For example, multiplication is a shortcut for repeated addition. In this lesson, you will use exponents as a shortcut for repeated multiplication.

Goals for This Lesson
- Simplify a numerical expression involving exponents.
- Evaluate a variable expression involving exponents.
- Write a number as a power of a given number.

Graded Activities in This Lesson
Lesson Quiz (computer-scored)

Materials
Intermediate Mathematics C: A Reference Guide and Problem Sets, pages 15–19

Optional
Positive Exponents Solutions

Calculator

Keywords
base: a number that is raised to some power (for example, in 5^3, 5 is the base)

exponent: a number that shows how many times the base is used as a factor

power of a number: the product when a number is multiplied by itself a given number of times (e.g., 5^3 or 5 • 5 • 5 is the third power of five)

factor: any of two or more numbers multiplied to form a product

Groundwork: Preparing for the Lesson [online]
You will review the steps in the order of operations.

Learn: Working with Positive Exponents [online]

As you work through this activity, answer the question below and record any notes in the space provided.

Summarize what you learned in this activity.

1. How can you write 243 as a power of 3?

MathCast: Evaluating a Variable Expression with Exponents [online]

View the video to see how to solve a typical problem.

Worked Examples: Positive Exponents [online]

Use the space below to work through the examples you see in the online screens.

Summary: Positive Exponents [online]

You can use exponents to simplify an expression that involves repeated multiplication. The exponent tells you how many times to use the base as a factor.

Any number to the zero power equals 1.

Any number to the first power equals the number.

Offline Learning: Positive Exponents [offline]

Read pages 15–18 in the Reference Guide.

Problem Sets

Complete Problems 1–29 odd and 32 on pages 18–19.

Lesson Assessment: Positive Exponents Quiz [online]

Now go back online to complete the lesson quiz.

Student Guide

Negative Exponents

It's one thing to evaluate expressions and solve equations containing *positive* exponents; in this lesson, you will learn to evaluate expressions and solve equations containing *negative* exponents. If you think negative exponents are like negative integers, you may be surprised.

Goals for the Lesson
- Simplify an expression involving negative exponents.
- Solve an equation involving negative exponents.

Graded Activities in This Lesson
Lesson Quiz (computer-scored)

Materials
Intermediate Mathematics C: A Reference Guide and Problem Sets, pages 20–23

Optional
Calculator

Keywords
base: a number that is raised to some power (for example, in 5^3, 5 is the base)

exponent: a number that shows how many times the base is used as a factor

Groundwork: Preparing for the Lesson [online]
You will review positive exponents.

Learn: Expressions with Negative Exponents [online]
You will learn the properties of negative exponents.

Summarize what you learned in this activity.

1. Write the three properties of negative exponents.

2. How are a^n and a^{-n} related? What is the product of a^n and a^{-n}?

Learn: Equations with Exponents [online]

You will learn how to solve equations that involve exponents.

Summarize what you learned in this activity.

1. If $2^3 = 8$ and $2^x = 8$, what is the value of x? How do you know?

MathCast: Solve an Equation [online]

View the video to see how to solve a typical problem.

Summary: Negative Exponents [online]

In this lesson, you learned how to work with negative exponents. To simplify expressions or solve equations containing negative exponents, use the properties of negative exponents.

Offline Learning: Negative Exponents [offline]

Read pages 20–22 in the reference guide.

Problem Sets
Complete Problems 1–8 and 22–25 on pages 22–23.

Extra Practice (optional)
Complete Problems 9–13 and 26–27 on pages 22–23 for extra practice (optional).

Lesson Assessment: Negative Exponents Quiz [online]

Now go back online to complete the lesson quiz.

Student Guide

Core Focus: Working with Exponents

You've learned how to simplify powers involving positive and negative exponents. Now it's time to learn about their properties. In this lesson, you will learn how to use the properties of exponents to multiply powers, divide powers, and raise a power to another power.

Goals for This Lesson
- Use the product of powers property to multiply powers.
- Use the quotient of powers property to divide powers.
- Use the power of a power property to raise a power to another power.

Graded Activities in This Lesson
Lesson Quiz (computer-graded)

Materials
Intermediate Mathematics C: A Reference Guide and Problem Sets, pages 24–26.

Keywords
none

Groundwork: Preparing for the Lesson [online]
You will simplify expressions involving positive and negative exponents.

Learn: Properties of Exponents [online]
Use the spaces below to take notes during this activity.

The Core Concept

Overview

Multiplying Powers

Dividing Powers

Raising a Power to a Power

Summary

Worked Examples: Properties of Exponents [online]
Use the space below to work through the examples you see in the online screens.

Offline Learning: Core Focus: Working with Exponents [offline]

Read pages 24–26.

Problem Sets

Complete Problems 1–12 on page 27.

Lesson Assessment [online]

Go back online to complete the Lesson Quiz

Student Guide

Scientific Notation

At any moment, there are an estimated 10,000,000,000,000,000,000 live insects in the world. Because this number has so many zeros, it would be easy to make a mistake when copying it down. Scientists often work with numbers that are either very large or very small and have many zeros. They do not lose time copying zeros because they write the numbers in scientific notation.

Goals for This Lesson
- Write a whole number or decimal number using scientific notation.
- Write a number given in scientific notation as a whole or decimal number.
- Multiply, divide, add, and subtract numbers given in scientific notation.

Graded Activities in This Lesson
Lesson Quiz (computer-scored)

Materials
Intermediate Mathematics C: A Reference Guide and Problem Sets, pages 27–30

Optional
calculator

Keywords
none

Groundwork: Preparing for the Lesson [online]
You will review how to multiply a decimal by a power of 10.

Learn: Converting Between Forms [online]

Summarize what you learned in this activity.

1. A number written in scientific notation is a product of two numbers.

   - The first number is

     _____.

   - The second number is a _____.

2. To convert a number from scientific notation to decimal form, _____.

   - If the exponent of 10 is positive, move the decimal point to the _____.
   - If the exponent of 10 is negative, move the decimal point to the _____.

3. To convert a number from decimal form to scientific notation, you must determine the two
   _____ that form the product.

   - Insert a decimal point after the first _____ to make a number greater than or
     equal to 1 but less than 10.

   - Count the number of places from the new decimal point you inserted to the
     _____ decimal point. Make the exponent _____ if you
     moved the decimal point to the right and make it _____ if you moved the
     decimal point to the left.

Learn: Performing Operations [online]

Summarize what you learned in this activity.

1. The process of adding numbers in scientific notation is similar to adding _____, in

   which the _____ is the variable part of the term.

2. What do you do if the result is not in scientific notation?

3. Add. Write the result in scientific notation.

$$3.6 \times 10^8 + 2.45 \times 10^8$$

4. Subtract. Write the result in scientific notation.

$$8.1 \times 10^{14} - 3.6 \times 10^{14}$$

5. Add. Write the result in scientific notation.

$$5.06 \times 10^{11} + 7 \times 10^{11}$$

6. Add. Write the result in scientific notation.

$$1.5 \times 10^7 + 2.6 \times 10^8$$

7. Use _____ when multiplying and dividing numbers in scientific notation.

8. Multiply. Write the result in scientific notation.

$$\left(4.03 \times 10^5\right)\left(2.5 \times 10^9\right)$$

9. Divide. Write the result in scientific notation.

$$\frac{9 \times 10^{15}}{3 \times 10^8}$$

Worked Examples: Scientific Notation [online]

Use the space below to work through the examples you see in the online screens.

Summary: Scientific Notation [online]

Scientific notation is a way to write very large and very small numbers in a compact form. To convert from scientific notation to decimal form, multiply the first number in the product by the given power of 10. If the exponent is positive, move the decimal point that number of places to the right. If the exponent is negative, move the decimal point that number of places to the left.

To convert from decimal form to scientific notation, insert the decimal point after the first nonzero digit and multiply by the power of 10 that will move the decimal point back to its original position.

To add and subtract numbers in scientific notation, rewrite one of the numbers, if necessary, so that both numbers have the same power of 10. Then add or subtract the numbers using the distributive property.

To multiply and divide numbers in scientific notation, use the properties of exponents to add and subtract the exponents.

Offline Learning: Scientific Notation [offline]

Read pages 27–29 in the Reference Guide.

Problem Sets

Complete Problems 1–33 odd on pages 29–30.

Extra Practice (optional)
Complete Problems 2–32 even on pages 29–30.

Lesson Assessment: Scientific Notation Quiz [online]

Now go back online to complete the lesson quiz.

Student Guide

Orders of Magnitude

There are different ways to estimate numbers. One way to estimate is to round. In this lesson, you will combine what you know about rounding and what you know about writing numbers in scientific notation to estimate numbers as the product of a single digit and a power of 10.

In addition, you will learn how to estimate a number as just a power of 10. This type of rough estimate is called an order-of-magnitude estimate.

Goals for This Lesson
- Estimate a quantity as the product of a single digit and a power of 10.

- Compare numbers that are expressed as the product of a single digit and a power of 10.

- Determine the best order-of-magnitude estimate for a number.

Graded Activities in This Lesson
Lesson Quiz (computer-scored)

Materials
Intermediate Mathemtics C: A Reference Guide and Problem Sets, pages 31–33

Optional
calculator

Keywords
order-of-magnitude estimate: a calculation that provides an answer that is accurate to the nearest power of 10

scientific notation: a method of expressing a number as the product of a number greater than or equal to 1 and less than 10, and a power of 10

Groundwork: Preparing for the Lesson [online]
You will write numbers in scientific notation.

Learn: Estimating and Comparing Large and Small Numbers [online]
You will estimate and compare very large and very small numbers by expressing them as products of a single digit and a power of 10.

Summarize what you learned in this activity.

1. How do you estimate a number as the product of a single digit and a power of 10?

2. How do you compare numbers that are each expressed as the product of a single digit and a power of 10?

Worked Examples: Estimating and Comparing Large and Small Numbers [online]

Use the space below to work through the examples you see in the online screens.

Learn: Order-of-Magnitude Estimates [online]

You will learn how to determine the best order-of-magnitude estimate of a number.

Summarize what you learned in this activity.

What are the steps for finding the best order-of-magnitude estimate of a number?

Worked Examples: Order-of-Magnitude Estimates [online]

Use the space below to work through the examples you see in the online screens.

MathCast: Order-of-Magnitude Estimates [online]

View the video to see how to solve a typical problem.

Summary: Order-of-Magnitude Estimates [online]

You can estimate a large or small number as the product of a single digit and a power of 10.

To find the best order-of-magnitude estimate of a number, determine the power of 10 to which the number is nearest in value.

Offline Learning: Order-of-Magnitude Estimates [offline]

Read pages 31–33 in the reference guide.

Problem Sets

Complete Problems 1–19 odd on page 33.

Extra Practice (optional)
Complete Problems 2–18 even on page 33.

Lesson Assessment: Order-of-Magnitude Quiz [online]

Go back online to complete the Lesson Assessment.

Student Guide

Core Focus: Working with Scientific Notation

Light travels at a speed of about 3×10^8 m/s. What would you do if you wanted to know how many kilometers light travels in a year? What would you do if you wanted to know how many years it would take for light to travel 1×10^{15} km? To solve problems like these, you must multiply or divide numbers expressed in scientific notation, and you must use a process that allows you to convert meters to kilometers and seconds to years. In this lesson, you will learn how to solve real-world problems that involve numbers expressed in scientific notation and you will use a process called dimensional analysis to convert units of measurement.

Goals for This Lesson

- Use dimensional analysis to convert units of measurement when quantities are expressed in scientific notation.

- Interpret numbers expressed in scientific notation on a calculator.

Graded Activities in This Lesson
Lesson Assessment (computer-graded)

Materials
Intermediate Mathematics C: A Reference Guide and Problem Sets, pages 36–38

Optional
calculator

Keywords and Pronunciation
none

Groundwork: Preparing for the Lesson [online]
You will multiply and divide numbers expressed in scientific notation.

Learn: Scientific Notation and Dimensional Analysis [online]
Use the spaces below to take notes during this activity.

Core Concept

Overview

Solving Problems Involving Scientific Notation

Summary

Worked Examples: Scientific Notation and Dimensional Analysis

[online]
Use the space below to work through the examples you see in the online screens.

Offline Learning: Core Focus: Working with Scientific Notation

[offline]
Read pages 34–36.

Problem Sets
Complete Problems 1–4 on page 37.

Lesson Assessment: Core Focus: Working with Scientific Notation Quiz [online]
Go back online to complete the Lesson Quiz.

Student Guide

Core Focus: Comparing Big and Small Numbers

How many times greater is the population of India than the population of Sweden? How many times greater is the distance between the sun and the earth than the distance between the earth and the moon? How many times greater is the mass of a caffeine molecule than the mass of a water molecule? All of these questions involve finding the number of times one very large or very small number is greater than another very large or very small number. This lesson will give you the tools to solve these types of problems.

Goals for This Lesson
* Determine the number of times greater one number is than another number using very large or very small numbers.

Graded Activities in This Lesson
There is no graded activity associated with this lesson.

Materials
Intermediate Mathematics C: A Reference Guide and Problem Sets, pages 38–39.

Optional
calculator

Keywords
none

Learn: Finding the Number of Times Greater [online]
Use the spaces below to take notes during this activity.

Core Focus

Overview

Finding the Number of Times Greater

Summary

Offline Learning: Core Focus: Comparing Big and Small Numbers [offline]

Read pages pages 38–39.

Problem Sets

Complete Problems 1–4 on page 39.

Student Guide

Unit Review

In this unit, you learned how to use the order of operations to simplify expressions, how to identify and combine like terms, how to simplify expressions involving positive and negative exponents, how to write numbers in scientific notation, how to estimate and compare very large or very small numbers, how to find the best order-of-magnitude estimate of a number, how to convert units when quantities are written in scientific notation, and how to estimate the number of times one number is greater than another number. Now it's time to pull together what you have learned.

Goals for This Lesson

- Simplify a numerical expression without grouping symbols.
- Simplify a numerical expression with grouping symbols.
- Place grouping symbols in an expression to create a specific value.
- Identify like terms.
- Simplify an expression using the distributive property.
- Collect like terms.
- Simplify a numerical expression involving positive exponents.
- Evaluate a variable expression involving positive exponents.
- Write a number as a power of a given number.
- Simplify an expression involving negative exponents.
- Solve an equation involving negative exponents.
- Use the product of powers property to multiply powers.
- Use the quotient of powers property to divide powers.
- Use the power to a power property to raise a power to another power.
- Write a whole or decimal number using scientific notation.
- Write a number given in scientific notation as a whole or decimal number.
- Multiply, divide, add, and subtract numbers given in scientific notation.
- Estimate a quantity as a product of a single digit and a power of 10.
- Compare numbers that are expressed as the product of a single digit and a power of 10.
- Determine the best order-of-magnitude estimate for a number.
- Use dimensional analysis to convert units when quantities are expressed in scientific notation.
- Interpret numbers expressed in scientific notation on a calculator.
- For very large or very small numbers, determine the number of times greater one number is than another number.

Graded Activities in This Lesson
There is no graded activity associated with this lesson.

Materials
Intermediate Mathematics C: A Reference Guide and Problem Sets, pages 40–41

Keywords
base: a number that is raised to some power (for example, in 5^3, 5 is the base)

grouping symbols: devices, such as parentheses, brackets, and fraction bars, used to set apart an expression that should be simplified before other operations are performed

order-of-magnitude estimate: a calculation that provides an answer that is accurate to the nearest power of 10

power of a number: the product when a number is multiplied by itself a given number of times

(e.g., 5^3 or 5 • 5 • 5 is the third power of five)

Unit Review: Practice Quiz [online]
The last screen of the Practice Quiz will show you how many times you attempted each problem. For each problem, record your number of attempts below. Complete the activities and reference guide problems that correspond with the Practice Quiz problems that took you more than one attempt. Check off the review activities and review problems as you complete them.

Problem 1
Attempts: _____
□ Complete review activities online
□ Complete Problems 1–10 on page 9

Problem 2
Attempts: _____
□ Complete review activities online
□ Complete Problems 13–21 on page 14

Problem 3
Attempts: _____
□ Complete review activities online
□ Complete Problems 26–29 on page 19

Problem 4
Attempts: _____
□ Complete review activities online
□ Complete Problems 22–27 on page 23

Problem 5
Attempts: _____
□ Complete review activities online
□ Complete Problems 13–16 on page 22

Problem 6
Attempts: _____
□ Complete review activities online
□ Complete Problems 13–24 on page 30

Problem 7
Attempts: _____
□ Complete review activities online
□ Complete Problems 25–30 on page 30

Problem 8
Attempts: _____
□ Complete review activities online
□ Complete Problems 12–17 on page 33

Problem 9
Attempts: _____
□ Complete review activities online
□ Complete Problems 1–4 on page 37

Problem 10
Attempts: _____
□ Complete review activities online
□ Complete Problems 1–4 on page 39

Offline Learning: Practice: Number Properties Review [online]

Complete all the Chapter Review problems on pages 40–41. Use the Topic Lookup at the bottom of page 41 to review topics for any problems that were difficult for you.

Student Guide

Unit Test

You have learned about simplifying expressions involving grouping symbols, positive and negative exponents, and like terms. You have also learned about expressing numbers in scientific notation, converting units for numbers expressed in scientific notation, and comparing and estimating very large or very small numbers. Now it's time to take the Unit Test.

This Unit Test has two parts—one part that will be scored by the computer and one part that your Learning Coach will score. You will complete the computer-scored part in this lesson.

Goals for This Lesson

- Simplify a numerical expression without grouping symbols.
- Simplify a numerical expression with grouping symbols.
- Place grouping symbols in an expression to create a specific value.
- Simplify an expression involving variable terms and constants.
- Simplify an expression using the distributive property.
- Simplify a numerical expression involving positive exponents.
- Evaluate a variable expression involving positive exponents.
- Write a number as a power of a given number.
- Simplify an expression and solve an equation involving negative exponents.
- Use the product of powers property to multiply powers.
- Use the quotient of powers property to divide powers.
- Use the power to a power property to raise a power to another power.
- Write a whole or decimal number using scientific notation.
- Write a number given in scientific notation as a whole or decimal number.
- Multiply, divide, add, and subtract numbers given in scientific notation.
- Determine the best order-of-magnitude estimate for a number.
- Interpret numbers expressed in scientific notation on a calculator.

Graded Activities in This Lesson

Number Properties Unit Test, Part 1

Number Properties Unit Test, Part 2

Unit Assessment: Number Properties, Part 1 [online]

You will complete a test covering the main goals of this unit. This part of the test is online. It will be scored by the computer.

Unit Assessment: Number Properties, Part 2 [offline]

This part of the Unit Test is offline.

1. Complete each question on your own. Make sure to show all your work.

2. Submit this part to your Learning Coach for a grade.

Student Guide

Extended Problems: Reasoning

In this lesson, you'll complete Extended Problems: Reasoning for the Number Properties unit.

Goals for This Lesson
- Analyze complex problems using mathematical knowledge and skills.

Graded Activities in This Lesson
Extended Problems: Reasoning

Extended Problems Graded Assignment [offline]
You will complete a graded assignment that focuses on reasoning in math.

Your Learning Coach will score this assignment.

- **Complete** the assignment on your own.
- **Submit** the completed assignment to your Learning Coach.

Student Guide

Addition and Subtraction Equations

Can you balance a twirling basketball on the end of your finger? Do you eat a balanced diet? Have you seen people scratch their heads as they try to balance a checkbook? Balance is an idea that you already think about and can apply to many different situations. Equations must maintain balance to be called "equations."

Goals for This Lesson

- Solve addition or subtraction equations.

- Solve addition or subtraction equations involving simplification.

- Write an equation that models a word problem involving addition or subtraction.

- Solve a word problem involving addition or subtraction.

Graded Activities in This Lesson

Lesson Quiz (computer-scored)

Materials

Intermediate Mathematics C: A Reference Guide and Problem Sets, pages 47–50

Optional

A Guide to Problem Solving
Using Algebra Tiles
Algebra Tiles – square and rectangular algebra tiles
calculator

Keywords

equation: a statement formed by placing an equals symbol between two numerical or variable expressions

equivalent equations: equations that have the same solution

solution: the value of a variable that makes an equation or inequality a true sentence

transformation: an operation performed on an equation or an inequality that produces a simpler equivalent statement

transform an equation: to rewrite an equation or inequality as an equivalent equation or inequality

transformation by addition: adding the same real number to each side of a given equation or inequality

transformation by subtraction: subtracting the same real number from each side of a given equation or inequality

Groundwork: Preparing for the Lesson [online]

You will review adding and subtracting integers in preparation for solving addition and subtraction equations.

Learn: Transformations [online]

You will learn how to use inverse operations to transform equations into simpler, equivalent equations.

When you solve an equation, your goal is to find the value of the variable that makes the equation true. Suppose you were asked to solve the equation $x + 2 = 5$. You would say the solution is $x = 3$. When you replace x with 3, you get $3 + 2 = 5$...a true statement. Notice that the solution $x = 3$ is also an equation.

What can you do to the equation $x + 2 = 5$ to get the equivalent equation $x = 3$? You can apply the properties of equality for addition or subtraction! How? See if you can figure it out using algebra tiles.

Directions for using the Algebra Tiles Learning Tool

1. Type the left side of the given equation in the left expression box.
2. Type the right side of the equation in the right expression box.
3. Click Build.
4. Add positive or negative tiles to the left and/or right side of the equation by dragging them from the box on the right side of the screen.
5. Look at how the equation changed. Write down the new equation.
6. Continue adding tiles to both sides, keeping the equation balanced, until x is by itself on one side of the equation.
7. Enter the solution and click Check.

Solve using algebra tiles. Answer the questions that follow each equation.

1. $x + 2 = 5$

How many and what type of algebra tiles did you add to the left side of the equation?

How many and what type of algebra tiles did you add to the right side of the equation?

What is the solution?

2. $3 = x - 5$

How many and what type of algebra tiles did you add to the left side of the equation?

How many and what type of algebra tiles did you add to the right side of the equation?

What is the solution?

3. $x - 2 = -6$

How many and what type of algebra tiles did you add to the left side of the equation?

How many and what type of algebra tiles did you add to the right side of the equation?

What is the solution?

Summarize what you learned in this activity.

1. What does it mean to solve an equation?

2. Show how transformations can be used to solve the equation $x + 2 = 7$. What is important about the equation $x = 5$?

3. Show how you can check the solution $x = 5$ for the original equation $x + 2 = 7$.

4. To solve the equation $x - 6 = 14 - 8$, what transformation should you use? Why?

5. Show the steps for solving the equation $x - 6 = 14 - 8$, and provide a check for the solution.

6. Define the addition property of equality and the subtraction property of equality.

　　　Addition Property of Equality –

　　　Subtraction Property of Equality –

7. Why are these properties important for solving equations?

8. The addition property of equality and the subtraction property of equality are equivalent properties, making the subtraction property of equality almost unnecessary. Why?

Worked Examples: Try Transformations [online]

In this activity, you will practice solving equations using addition or subtraction.

Use the space below to work through the examples you see in the online screens.

Learn: Solving Real-World Problems [online]

You will learn to use equations that involve addition or subtraction as well as the problem-solving plan to solve a real-world problem.

Use the problem-solving plan to solve this problem.

At the grocery store you bought a pack of gum ($0.79), a chunk of cheese ($1.85), and an orange ($0.56). You handed the checkout person a $5 bill and received $1.70 in change. Is your change correct?

1. Identify.

2. Strategize.

3. Set Up.

4. Solve.

5. Check.

Worked Examples: Try Solving Real-World Problems [online]

You will have the opportunity to practice solving equations using addition or subtraction, as well as a real-world problem.

Use this space to show your work before checking your answers against those provided online.

Summary: Addition and Subtraction Equations [online]

Transformations are used to solve equations.

You can use the addition property of equality and the subtraction property of equality to find equivalent equations that make it easy to see solutions.

Combined with good problem solving, transformations allow you to solve a significant number of real-world problems.

Offline Learning: Addition and Subtraction Equations [offline]

In the Book
Read pages 47–49 in the reference guide.

Problem Sets
Complete Problems 1–29 odd on page 50.

Extra Practice (optional)
Complete Problems 2–28 even on page 50.

Lesson Assessment: Addition and Subtraction Equations Quiz

[online]
Now go back online to complete the Lesson Quiz.

Name _____ Date _____

A Guide to Problem Solving

Do you know people who seem to solve math problems with little effort? Perhaps you are one of those people.

Few problems in the real world, however, are in the form of an equation you just solve. In fact, the easiest part of solving a problem might be the last part—solving the equation. The key is learning where to start when you don't know how to set up an equation.

Remember: When solving a problem, writing the correct equation is at least as important as performing the calculations correctly.

As you gain more experience in problem solving, you will recognize that many problems are similar to each other. The strategies that you use to solve one problem will be useful in solving another, if they are the same type of problem. Below are examples of strategies that can be used.

You don't need to memorize the word problems presented here or the names of the strategies, but it is important that you recognize their characteristics. When you see similar problems later, you can draw upon this information to help you.

Experimentation and Simulation

Problem 1: A doctor gave Mr. Ache 8 tablets and instructed him to take one every 3 hours, starting immediately in the doctor's office. If Mr. Ache does as he is told, how long will it be until he has taken all of the tablets?

The apparent answer is 24 hours, but is that correct? By simulating the problem with a diagram, you can check your answer.

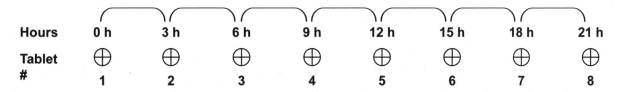

Hours	0 h	3 h	6 h	9 h	12 h	15 h	18 h	21 h
Tablet #	1	2	3	4	5	6	7	8

Count up the hours. The correct answer is 21 hours, not 24 hours. Mr. Ache takes the first tablet and *then* starts the 3-hour intervals.

You can also simulate this problem with candy pieces, eating one every 3 minutes starting now and timing the experiment from start to finish. (You might find that solving problems can be more fun than you thought!)

Problem 2: You are to erect a fence 100 feet long, placing the fence poles 10 feet apart. How many poles will you need to complete the task?

The apparent answer is 10, but is that correct? You can create a diagram to find out.

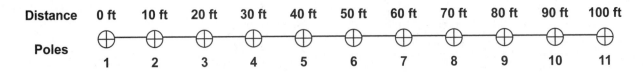

You can see from the diagram that you will need 11 poles to complete this task, not 10.

Compare and contrast this fence pole problem and the tablet problem above. Can you see that knowing how to solve one of them can help you more easily solve the other and any future problems similar to these?

Computers and calculators can assist greatly with experimentation and simulation models. Now think about whether a computer could solve a problem, even a simple one like the two examples, without being given information in a language and form that it can process. Can you see how important it is to set up a problem correctly before attempting to solve it?

Remember: You can solve problems by identifying relationships, distinguishing between relevant and irrelevant information, identifying missing information, sequencing and prioritizing information, and observing patterns.

Simplification and Reduction

Problem: Big Bowl stadium seats 100,000 people. At the game, ushers estimate that there are 3 males seated for every 2 females in the sold-out stadium. How many males and how many females are in Big Bowl?

You know that—

	Males	Females
Rate	3 out of every 5 people are male	2 out of every 5 people are female
Multiply by 2	6 out of every 10 people are male	4 out of every 10 people are female
Multiply by 10	60 out of every 100 people are male	40 out of every 100 people are female

Because percent is an amount per 100, you now know that—

- 60% of 100,000 people or 60,000 people are male.
- 40% of 100,000 people or 40,000 people are female.

Pattern Recognition

Problem: Jason is having a party. The first time the doorbell rings, one guest enters. At each additional ring of the doorbell, a group enters that has two more people than the previous group had. How many total guests will have entered after the 18th ring?

A great way to discover patterns is to make a table, as follows:

Doorbell Ring	# Of Guests Arriving	Total # Of Guests
1	1	1
2	3	4
3	5	9
4	7	16
5	9	25
6	11	36
.	.	.
.	.	.
.	.	.

Do you notice a pattern? If so, you can go directly to the answer, rather than continuing with the table until you reach the 18th ring.

Compare the number of doorbell rings (first column) to the total number of guests who have arrived by that ring (third column). If r **equals** the number of doorbell rings, then—

r^2 = total number of guests who have arrived

Check it out!

So, the total number of guests after the 18th ring would be 18^2, which equals 324. Therefore, 324 guests will have arrived after 18 rings of the doorbell.

Remember: A problem may contain extra information that is not important to finding a solution. Identifying the necessary information in a problem is very important.

Guess and Test

Another strategy is the guess-and-test approach. You may be able to solve the next problem using mental math, with no pencil or paper required.

Problem: The Dubuque Dodgers and the Davenport Divers set a new semi-pro basketball league record last week when they scored 222 points between them in one game. If the Divers lost by 14 points, how many points did the Dodgers score?

One strategy in solving this problem is to just start guessing and try to come up with two scores that are separated by 14 points. If you stop to think for a minute, you will realize that out of 222 points, a difference of 14 points is not very much. The answer must be somewhere around one-half of 222. Using mental math, you can determine that 111 is the mean score. So, if you add and subtract 7 points to the mean score, you will see that the Dodgers scored 118 points ($111 + 7 = 118$) while the Divers scored 104 points ($111 - 7 = 104$ and $104 + 118 = 222$). Great game!

Logical Deduction

Logical Deduction is a valuable strategy. Although the problem that follows is more like a puzzle, the type of thinking required to solve it is one you will use and apply your entire life.

Problem: Justin, Jakob, Josh, Joey, and Jordan were the first five finishers of a 16-mile race. From the given clues, give the order in which they finished.

1. Justin passed Jakob just before the finish line.

2. Jordan finished 10 seconds ahead of Justin.

3. Joey crossed the finish line in a dead heat with Jakob.

4. Josh was fifth at the finish.

Do you know where to begin? Consider each fact in the order it is written.

If Justin passed Jakob just before the finish line, then Justin finished before Jakob.

- Order of finish: Justin, Jakob

If Jordan finished 10 seconds ahead of Justin, then—

- Order of finish: Jordan, Justin, Jakob

If Joey crossed the finish line a dead heat with Jakob, then—

- Order of finish: Jordan, Justin, Jakob/Joey (tie)

If Josh was fifth at the finish, then everyone beat Josh—

- Order of finish: Jordan, Justin, Jakob/Joey (tie), Josh

Working Backward

Working backward is a good example of thinking differently.

Problem: Jonathan computed his average for five tests in his math class and found he had earned a 76. What must he score on the final two tests to raise his average to 80?

If Jonathan had 5 tests that averaged 76, his total number of points would be 5×76 or 380. Think about why that is true. Jonathan has two additional tests in which to bring up his average. He knows that to average 80 on all seven tests, he would need a total of 560 points ($80 \times 7 = 560$). Since Jonathan already has 380 points, he will need a total of 180 more points ($560 - 380 = 180$). Therefore, he needs to get scores of 90, or any combination with a sum of 180, on each of his two remaining tests. Do you think he can do it?

Drawing a Diagram

Drawing a Diagram can really help you visualize a problem, as you saw in the problems about the medicine tablets and fence poles.

Problem: How much will it cost to cut a log into 8 equal pieces, if you know that cutting it into 4 equal pieces costs 60 cents? Each piece must be cut separately. (*Hint: Think about the tablet and fence pole problems.*)

Cutting a log into 4 equal pieces will cost 60 cents. How much is that per cut? Fifteen cents? Think again.

Cut #	1	2	3

Since it takes only 3 cuts to create 4 equal pieces, the cost is 20 cents (60 cents ÷ 3 = 20 cents).

So, how much will it cost to cut the log into 8 equal pieces?

Cut #	1	2	3	4	5	6	7

Seven cuts at 20 cents each equals $1.40. Did you get it right?

How is this problem similar to the medicine tablet and fence pole problems? Can you see that each one appears to lead to an answer that is off by one item or unit each time? Do you find these problems are easier to understand when you draw a diagram? Even if you know the answer, drawing a diagram sometimes provides a great way to check your work.

Remember: Once the mathematical model has been solved, translating the result into a meaningful answer to the original equation is the crucial final step.

No Solution

Some problems don't have a solution!

Problem: Speedy drives 2 miles to work each morning. He must average 30 miles per hour to get to work on time. One morning, a slow driver gets in his way for the first mile, cutting his average to 15 mph. He tries to calculate the speed he'll need to drive for the rest of the trip to arrive on time. His car can go up to 120 mph. How fast must he drive the final mile?

Although this may seem like a somewhat complicated problem, it can be figured out in a number of ways. One of the simpler ways is to first figure out how long Speedy's trip normally takes. If he travels 2 miles each day at 30 mph, the trip will normally take 4 minutes, according to the formula:

$$\text{rate} \times \text{time} = \text{distance}$$
$$rt = d$$
$$30t = 2$$
$$t = \frac{2}{30} = \frac{1}{15} \text{ of an hour and } \frac{1}{15} \text{ hrs} \times \frac{60 \text{ minutes}}{1 \text{ hour}} = \frac{60}{15} = 4 \text{ minutes}$$

Then figure out how much time the first mile takes on the day that the driver slows Speedy down to 15 mph:

$$rt = d$$
$$15t = 1$$
$$t = \frac{1}{15} \text{ of an hour}$$

You already know that $\frac{1}{15}$ of an hour is 4 minutes, so there is no amount of speed that will get him to work on time. The first mile used all 4 minutes Speedy had allowed himself to get to work. His car could go 1000 mph, and Speedy would still be late.

Can you think of other ways to approach this problem?

Now that you have some effective strategies in mind, you can apply what you have learned to the five-step Plan for Solving a Word Problem.

Plan for Solving a Word Problem

Step 1 Read the problem carefully. Decide what unknown numbers are asked for and what facts are known. Making a sketch may help (or using one of the other strategies you have now learned).

Step 2 Choose a variable and use it with the given facts to represent the unknowns described in the problem.

Step 3 Reread the problem and write an equation that represents relationships among the numbers in the problem.

Step 4 Solve the equation and find the unknowns asked for.

Step 5 Check your results with the words of the problem. Give the answer.

Why Learn Problem Solving?

You may ask, "Why not simply rely on technology to solve the problems?" It is true that computers and calculators can solve long, difficult, monotonous problems, but only if they are given proper information and told exactly what to do. In other words, if you ask a computer for an answer, the answer will be only as correct as the instructions and facts you supply. Computer programmers sometimes use a term for what happens when the instructions and information given to a computer are wrong: "garbage in, garbage out." Calculators and computers know nothing more than what they are told, and they follow directions very well—both good directions and bad ones.

Problems without words are just numbers to be manipulated or equations to be solved. Do you know of any job where a person is paid to sit and just crunch numbers? We have wonderful technology to do that. Employers want men and women who can think critically, problem solve, dream, and invent. Develop your mind to think and work in different ways. Dare to be a visionary. The world is begging for people who can do these things. Are you willing to work to become one of them?

Five Characteristics of a Great Problem Solver

1. FLUENCY – The ability to find different ways to solve problems. Is there more than one answer? How many different approaches can you use?

2. FLEXIBILITY – The ability to look at a problem in a different way. Watch and listen to how others approach problems and learn from them. It is easy to think that everybody thinks just as you do, but it is not true. Collect a toolbox of different strategies to solve problems.

3. ORIGINALITY – The ability to think of a unique response. As you listen to others' ideas, you will learn different ways of thinking.

4. APPLICABILITY – The ability to elaborate on a problem by rephrasing it and using prior knowledge.

5. DILIGENCE/DRIVE – The ability to stick with a problem through mistakes, incorrect attempts, and "getting stuck" to finally solve it. Success and invention often come after a series of mistakes and false assumptions. The only time a mistake is a problem is when it is your last attempt. Do not give up!

Use the checklist below to help you develop your problem-solving skills! You may want to print multiple copies of this page to use throughout the course while solving problems.

In this guide, you have explored a number of problem-solving strategies, received a variety of tips for success, and reviewed the five-step Plan for Solving a Word Problem.

Below is a helpful checklist to bring all the information together that you've learned to help you develop into a great problem solver. As you use the checklist to remind yourself of how to approach problems, your problem-solving skills will improve not only in this course but also in all aspects of study.

Prior to solving the problem:

☐ Read the problem more than once.

☐ Be sure you understand what the problem says.

☐ Restate the problem in your own words.

☐ Try to remember a similar problem you have worked.

☐ Identify the information that directly applies to solving this problem.

☐ Disregard information you don't need.

As you solve the problem:

☐ Think about the steps required to solve the problem.

☐ Check your work as you go.

☐ Stop and rethink your steps.

Try different strategies:

☐ Experiment and simulate.

☐ Simplify and reduce the problem.

☐ Recognize a pattern in the problem.

☐ Guess and check.

☐ Use logical deduction.

☐ Work the problem backward.

☐ Draw a picture.

☐ Apply your own unique strategies.

After solving the problem:

☐ Check to see that your calculations are correct.

☐ Ask yourself whether your answer is reasonable.

☐ Solve the problem another way and compare the solutions.

Most of all, enjoy the experience.

Name _____ Date _____

Algebra Tiles

cut

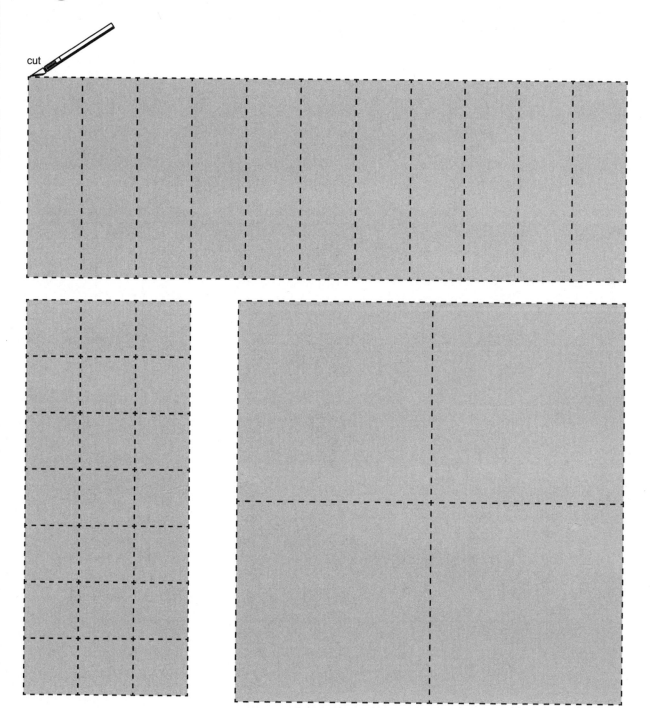

Name _____   Date _____

Algebra Tiles: Instructions

If possible, print the tiles on card stock and laminate them for future use. For safety reasons, have an adult use a utility craft knife and a straightedge to cut along the dotted lines.

Note that in the first group of tiles, each rectangular tile represents an area of x square units.

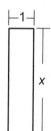

Area = Length • Width
$$= 1 \bullet x$$
$$= x$$

In the second group of tiles, each small square tile represents an area of 1 square unit.

Area = Length • Width
$$= 1 \bullet 1$$
$$= 1$$

In the third group, each larger square tile represents an area of x^2 square units.

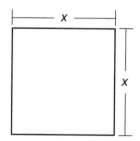

Area = Length • Width
$$= x \bullet x$$
$$= x^2$$

Find a good place to keep these tiles. You'll be using them throughout Algebra 1.

The plain side of the tiles ☐ represents a positive unit, and the shaded side ■ (the front of the printed tile sheet) represents a negative unit.

When using the tiles to model algebraic expressions, you may find it helpful to write out the original problem before you model the problem with the tiles. Making a sketch of your original problem is also useful. Remember to write the procedure and solution in algebraic symbols.

Keep in mind that using the tiles is a way for you to "see" the algebra modeled. The tiles help only to introduce an idea and create a visual concept. Beyond that, problems will become too complicated to model, so it is important to learn the patterns of algebraic solutions beyond what can be shown with tiles.

Student Guide

Core Focus: Addition and Subtraction Equations

You can apply the distributive property and combine like terms to simplify one or both sides of an equation before you solve it.

Goal for This Lesson
- Solve addition or subtraction equations involving simplification.

Graded Activities in This Lesson
Lesson Assessment (computer-graded)

Materials
Intermediate Mathematics C: A Reference Guide and Problem Sets, pages 51–53

Keywords
none

Groundwork: Preparing for the Lesson [online]
You will practice simplifying expressions using the distributive property.

Learn: Simplifying Before Solving [online]
Use the space below to take notes during this activity.

Overview

Simplifying and Solving Equations

Summary

Worked Examples: Simplifying Before Solving [online]
Use the space below to work through the examples you see in the online screens.

Offline Learning: Core Focus: Addition and Subtraction Equations

[offline]
Read pages 51–52.

Problem Sets
Complete Problems 1–8 on page 53.

Lesson Assessment: Core Focus Addition and Subtraction Equations Quiz [online]
Go back online to complete the Lesson Assessment.

Student Guide

Multiplication and Division Equations, Part 1

You now know how to solve equations using transformations. Addition and subtraction are two types of mathematical transformations. They provide some of the tools you need for solving problems. Different tools solve different problems. Now you will build your "tool kit" by learning how to transform equations using multiplication and division.

Goals for This Lesson
- Solve an equation involving division.
- Solve an equation involving multiplication.

Graded Activities in This Lesson
Lesson Quiz (computer-scored)

Materials
Intermediate Mathematics C: A Reference Guide and Problem Sets, pages 54–56
calculator

Keywords
equivalent equations: equations that have the same solution

transformation by multiplication: multiplying each side of a given equation by the same nonzero real number

transformation by division: dividing each side of a given equation by the same nonzero real number

Groundwork: Preparing for the Lesson [online]
Solve a few typical multiplication and division problems.

Learn: Transformations: Multiplication and Division [online]
In this activity, you will learn how to solve equations using the multiplication and division properties of equality.

Solve the equations using algebra tiles. The directions for using the Algebra Tiles Learning Tool are provided below.

1. $2x = 6$

How many rows of x tiles did you have in the left column of the table?

How many rows of unit tiles did you have in the right column of the table?

How many unit tiles were in each row of the table?

What is the solution to the equation?

2. −4x = 12

How many rows of x tiles did you have in the left column of the table?

How many rows of unit tiles did you have in the right column of the table?

How many unit tiles were in each row of the table?

What is the solution to the equation?

Directions for using the Algebra Tiles Learning Tool:

1. Type the left side of the equation in the left expression box.

2. Type the right side of the equation in the right expression box.

3. Select Build.

4. Select the division symbol button to create one row for each multiple of *x*. For example, for 2*x*, you need two rows.

5. Drag an *x* tile to each new row in the left column so that there is one tile in each row.

6. Drag unit tiles to the new rows in the right column of the table. Only add tiles to rows where there are corresponding *x* tiles. Divide the unit tiles equally among these rows.

7. If the coefficient of *x* is negative, select Multiply by −1.

8. Look at one of the rows to determine what 1*x* equals. Enter your answer and check it.

Summarize what you learned in this activity.

1. Write an equation that is equivalent to $\dfrac{x}{4} = -3$.

2. State the multiplication property of equality.

3. State the division property of equality.

5. Why isn't the division property of equality a necessary property? (Select the Think About It link for the answer.)

Worked Examples: Try Simple Multiplication and Division Equations [online]

Use the space below to work through the examples you see in the online screens.

MathCast: Using Reciprocals [online]

View the video to see how to solve a typical problem.

Summary: Multiplication and Division Equations, Part 1 [online]

In this lesson, you learned how to use transformations to solve equations.

You can use the multiplication and division properties of equality to help you find equivalent equations that make it easy to find and see solutions.

Offline Learning: Multiplication and Division Equations, Part 1

[offline]

Read pages 54–55.

Do the Math

Consider the following equation:

$$3x = 15$$

This equation describes the relationship between a variable x and the numbers 3 and 15. What other ways are there of expressing this relationship?

Multiplication or division can help you express this relationship differently so that you can find the value of x. When you use an operation such as multiplication or division to transform an equation, you create an equivalent, usually simpler, equation.

Remember: *Equivalent equations have the same solution. You can change an equation in many ways to make new equations with exactly the same solution. Doing so can make a solution easier to see.*

When should you use multiplication to transform an equation? When should you divide? Whenever you want to divide, you can instead choose to multiply by a reciprocal. It doesn't matter which you do as long as you are careful. You can pick the approach that makes describing the solution set as easy as possible. Consider this exercise.

Solve for x.

$$600 = -25x$$

$600 = -25x$	Original equation
$\dfrac{600}{-25} = \dfrac{-25x}{-25}$	Divide both sides by -25 (or multiply by $\dfrac{1}{-25}$).
$-24 = x$	Simplify.
Check: $\quad 600 = -25(-24)$	
$600 = 600$	This is a true statement, so the solution is correct.

The solution set is $\{-24\}$.

You can either multiply by $-\dfrac{1}{25}$ or divide by -25 to create a value of $+1$ for the coefficient of x. The transformations of the equation are equal.

In the next exercise, multiplying by the reciprocal is the easiest way to solve the equation.

Solve for b.

$$-\frac{1}{8}b = 8$$

$-\dfrac{1}{8}b = 8$	Original equation
$-8\left(-\dfrac{1}{8}b\right) = -8(8)$	Multiply both sides by $-\dfrac{8}{1}$ or -8.
$b = -64$	Simplify.
Check: $\quad -\dfrac{1}{8}(-64) = 8$	
$8 = 8$	This is a true statement, so the solution is correct.

The solution set is {–64}.

Think About It: Why does the Check step verify that your answer is a solution to the original equation?

Finally, in this exercise, you can multiply by the reciprocal to create a value of +1 for the coefficient of *x*.

Solve for *x*.

$$99 = -\frac{11}{5}x$$

$99 = -\dfrac{11}{5}x$	Original equation
$-\dfrac{5}{11}(99) = -\dfrac{5}{11}\left(-\dfrac{11}{5}x\right)$	Multiply both sides by $-\dfrac{5}{11}$.
$-45 = x$	Simplify.

Check:

$99 = -\dfrac{11}{5}(-45)$	
$99 = 99$	This is a true statement, so the solution is correct.

The solution set is {–45}.

Did you know that multiplying an equation by zero creates a new equation that does not have the same solution set as the original equation? What's the big deal? Multiplying by zero makes both sides of an equation equal to zero. It basically destroys the relationship defined by the original equation. No other number does that. The point of a series of transformations is not just to find simpler true equations, but also to find simpler equivalent equations. Since multiplying an equation by zero does not create an equation with the same solution set as the original, it does not create equivalent equations. Never multiply by zero to transform an equation.

Answer to Think About It*: Solving an equation means finding values for the variable that make the equation a true statement. When you check an answer, you substitute the answer for the variable in the original equation. If the answer produces a true statement (i.e., the left side of the equation equals the right side of the equation), you know you have found a solution.*

Problem Sets
Complete Problems 1–18 on page 56.

Key It In (optional)

Always check the solutions to an equation. It's extra work, but your calculator can make the job a little easier. Here is how you can check the solutions to two of the examples on the previous pages of this Student Guide.

Check.

$600 = -25x$ Original equation

$600 = -25(-24)$ Substitute the solution for x in the original equation.

Use your calculator to evaluate the right-hand side of the equation.

Handheld Graphing Calculator: (–)   25   ×   (–)   24   ENTER

GraphCalc: (–   25   )   *   (–   24   )   ENTER

The right-hand side of the equation equals 600, so the solution checks out.

Check.

$-\dfrac{1}{8}b = 8$ Original equation.

$-\dfrac{1}{8}(-64) = 8$ Substitute the solution for b in the original equation.

Use your calculator to evaluate the left-hand side of the equation.

Handheld Graphing Calculator: (–)   1   ÷   8   ×   (–)   64   ENTER

GraphCalc: (–   1   /   8   )   *   (–   64   )   ENTER

The left-hand side of the equation equals 8, so the solution checks out.

Extension (optional)

Solve the equation.

$$5x = 75$$

Use your solution to the equation above to predict the solution for each equation below.

1. $0.5x = 7.5$

2. $0.05x = 0.75$

3. $50x = 750$

4. $0.5x = 75$

5. $5x = 7.5$

Lesson Assessment: Multiplication and Division Equations, Part 1
Quiz [online]
Now go back online to complete the Lesson Quiz.

Answers

Extension

You can use division to solve the equation.

$$5x = 75$$

$$\frac{5x}{5} = \frac{75}{5}$$

$$x = 15$$

The first three equations are equivalent to the above equation, so they have the same solution.

1. $x = 15$

2. $x = 15$

3. $x = 15$

The last two are similar except for the position of the decimal point in the answer.

4. $x = 150$

5. $x = 1.5$

Name

Date

Algebra Tiles

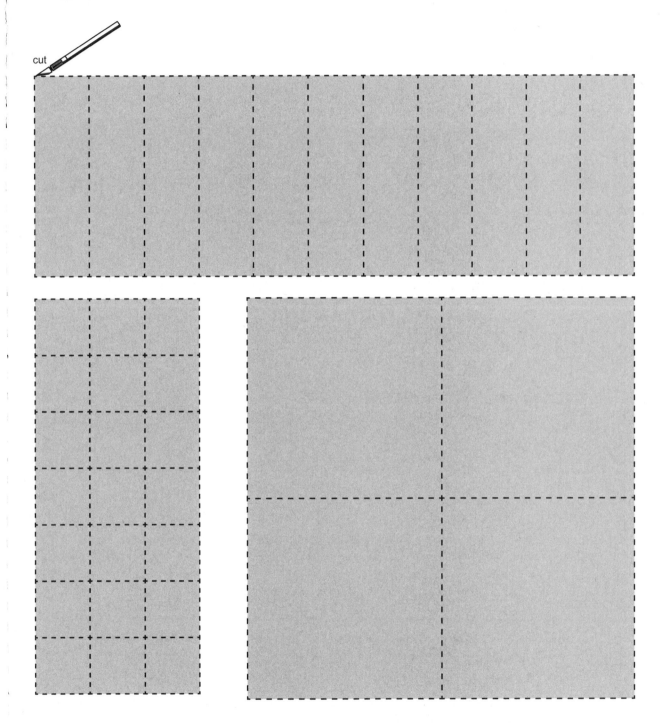

cut

Name _____   Date _____

Algebra Tiles: Instructions

If possible, print the tiles on card stock and laminate them for future use. For safety reasons, have an adult use a utility craft knife and a straightedge to cut along the dotted lines.

Note that in the first group of tiles, each rectangular tile represents an area of x square units.

Area = Length • Width
     = 1 • x
     = x

In the second group of tiles, each small square tile represents an area of 1 square unit.

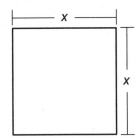

Area = Length • Width
     = 1 • 1
     = 1

In the third group, each larger square tile represents an area of x^2 square units.

Area = Length • Width
     = x • x
     = x^2

Find a good place to keep these tiles. You'll be using them throughout Algebra 1.

The plain side of the tiles ☐ represents a positive unit, and the shaded side ■ (the front of the printed tile sheet) represents a negative unit.

When using the tiles to model algebraic expressions, you may find it helpful to write out the original problem before you model the problem with the tiles. Making a sketch of your original problem is also useful. Remember to write the procedure and solution in algebraic symbols.

Keep in mind that using the tiles is a way for you to "see" the algebra modeled. The tiles help only to introduce an idea and create a visual concept. Beyond that, problems will become too complicated to model, so it is important to learn the patterns of algebraic solutions beyond what can be shown with tiles.

Student Guide

Multiplication and Division Equations, Part 2

Now you can solve equations using addition, subtraction, multiplication, and division. These processes let you change the form of an equation without destroying the equality of its members. Whether you use addition, subtraction, multiplication, or division properties of equality, you will not destroy the fact that the two sides of the equation are equal. Mathematicians call this transformation. Every day, people in many careers use transformations, but rarely do they simply solve algebra problems. Problems come from true situations. In this lesson, you will work on solving more problems that are practical, and to do this you will apply what you just learned.

Goals for This Lesson

- Write an equation that models a word problem involving multiplication or division.

- Solve a word problem that involves an equation with multiplication or division.

Graded Activities in This Lesson

Lesson Quiz (computer-scored)

Materials

Intermediate Mathematics C: A Reference Guide and Problem Sets, pages 56–57.

Optional

calculator

A Guide to Problem Solving

Keywords

equivalent equations: equations that have the same solution

transformation by division: dividing each side of a given equation by the same nonzero real number

transformation by multiplication: multiplying each side of a given equation by the same nonzero real number

Groundwork: Preparing for the Lesson [online]

Take this time to review translation of everyday language into mathematical expressions, as well as the steps involved in the problem-solving plan.

Use the spaces below to take notes during this activity.

Plan for Solving a Word Problem

       Step 1.

       Step 2.

       Step 3.

       Step 4.

       Step 5.

Learn: Solving More Real-World Problems [online]

Use the problem-solving plan to work through this problem.

Luis and two friends bought a foot-long sandwich for lunch. The store cut the sandwich into 8 equal pieces. Luis ate 3 pieces of the sandwich and paid $2.70 as his share of the cost. How much did the whole sandwich cost?

Identify.

Strategize.

Set Up.

Solve.

Check.

MathCast: Finding a Unit Price [online]

View the video to see how to solve a typical problem.

Worked Examples: Try Multiplication and Division Equations, Part 2 [online]

Use the space below to work through the examples you see in the online screens.

Summary: Multiplication and Division Equations, Part 2 [online]

In this lesson, you learned how to use transformations to solve equations.

When combined with good problem solving, transformations allow you to solve a significant number of real-world problems.

You can use multiplication and division equations to solve many real-world problems.

Offline Learning: Multiplication and Division Equations, Part 2

[offline]
Read page 56 in the reference guide.

Problem Sets
Complete Problems 19–23 on page 57.

Lesson Assessment: Multiplication and Division Equations, Part 2
Quiz [online]

Now go back online to complete the Lesson Quiz.

Name _____   Date _____

A Guide to Problem Solving

Do you know people who seem to solve math problems with little effort? Perhaps you are one of those people.

Few problems in the real world, however, are in the form of an equation you just solve. In fact, the easiest part of solving a problem might be the last part—solving the equation. The key is learning where to start when you don't know how to set up an equation.

Remember: When solving a problem, writing the correct equation is at least as important as performing the calculations correctly.

As you gain more experience in problem solving, you will recognize that many problems are similar to each other. The strategies that you use to solve one problem will be useful in solving another, if they are the same type of problem. Below are examples of strategies that can be used.

You don't need to memorize the word problems presented here or the names of the strategies, but it is important that you recognize their characteristics. When you see similar problems later, you can draw upon this information to help you.

Experimentation and Simulation

Problem 1: A doctor gave Mr. Ache 8 tablets and instructed him to take one every 3 hours, starting immediately in the doctor's office. If Mr. Ache does as he is told, how long will it be until he has taken all of the tablets?

The apparent answer is 24 hours, but is that correct? By simulating the problem with a diagram, you can check your answer.

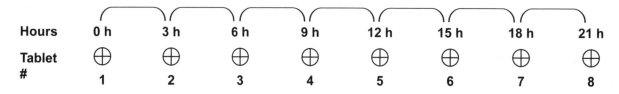

Count up the hours. The correct answer is 21 hours, not 24 hours. Mr. Ache takes the first tablet and *then* starts the 3-hour intervals.

You can also simulate this problem with candy pieces, eating one every 3 minutes starting now and timing the experiment from start to finish. (You might find that solving problems can be more fun than you thought!)

Problem 2: You are to erect a fence 100 feet long, placing the fence poles 10 feet apart. How many poles will you need to complete the task?

The apparent answer is 10, but is that correct? You can create a diagram to find out.

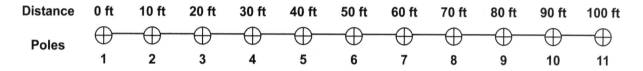

You can see from the diagram that you will need 11 poles to complete this task, not 10.

Compare and contrast this fence pole problem and the tablet problem above. Can you see that knowing how to solve one of them can help you more easily solve the other and any future problems similar to these?

Computers and calculators can assist greatly with experimentation and simulation models. Now think about whether a computer could solve a problem, even a simple one like the two examples, without being given information in a language and form that it can process. Can you see how important it is to set up a problem correctly before attempting to solve it?

Remember: You can solve problems by identifying relationships, distinguishing between relevant and irrelevant information, identifying missing information, sequencing and prioritizing information, and observing patterns.

Simplification and Reduction

Problem: Big Bowl stadium seats 100,000 people. At the game, ushers estimate that there are 3 males seated for every 2 females in the sold-out stadium. How many males and how many females are in Big Bowl?

You know that—

	Males	Females
Rate	3 out of every 5 people are male	2 out of every 5 people are female
Multiply by 2	6 out of every 10 people are male	4 out of every 10 people are female
Multiply by 10	60 out of every 100 people are male	40 out of every 100 people are female

Because percent is an amount per 100, you now know that—

• 60% of 100,000 people or 60,000 people are male.

• 40% of 100,000 people or 40,000 people are female.

Pattern Recognition

Problem: Jason is having a party. The first time the doorbell rings, one guest enters. At each additional ring of the doorbell, a group enters that has two more people than the previous group had. How many total guests will have entered after the 18th ring?

A great way to discover patterns is to make a table, as follows:

Doorbell Ring	# Of Guests Arriving	Total # Of Guests
1	1	1
2	3	4
3	5	9
4	7	16
5	9	25
6	11	36
.	.	.
.	.	.
.	.	.

Do you notice a pattern? If so, you can go directly to the answer, rather than continuing with the table until you reach the 18th ring.

Compare the number of doorbell rings (first column) to the total number of guests who have arrived by that ring (third column). If r **equals** the number of doorbell rings, then—

r^2 = total number of guests who have arrived

Check it out!

So, the total number of guests after the 18th ring would be 18^2, which equals 324. Therefore, 324 guests will have arrived after 18 rings of the doorbell.

Remember: A problem may contain extra information that is not important to finding a solution. Identifying the necessary information in a problem is very important.

Guess and Test

Another strategy is the guess-and-test approach. You may be able to solve the next problem using mental math, with no pencil or paper required.

Problem: The Dubuque Dodgers and the Davenport Divers set a new semi-pro basketball league record last week when they scored 222 points between them in one game. If the Divers lost by 14 points, how many points did the Dodgers score?

One strategy in solving this problem is to just start guessing and try to come up with two scores that are separated by 14 points. If you stop to think for a minute, you will realize that out of 222 points, a difference of 14 points is not very much. The answer must be somewhere around one-half of 222. Using mental math, you can determine that 111 is the mean score. So, if you add and subtract 7 points to the mean score, you will see that the Dodgers scored 118 points (111 + 7 = 118) while the Divers scored 104 points (111 − 7 = 104 and 104 + 118 = 222). Great game!

Logical Deduction

Logical Deduction is a valuable strategy. Although the problem that follows is more like a puzzle, the type of thinking required to solve it is one you will use and apply your entire life.

Problem: Justin, Jakob, Josh, Joey, and Jordan were the first five finishers of a 16-mile race. From the given clues, give the order in which they finished.

1. Justin passed Jakob just before the finish line.

2. Jordan finished 10 seconds ahead of Justin.

3. Joey crossed the finish line in a dead heat with Jakob.

4. Josh was fifth at the finish.

Do you know where to begin? Consider each fact in the order it is written.

If Justin passed Jakob just before the finish line, then Justin finished before Jakob.

- Order of finish: Justin, Jakob

If Jordan finished 10 seconds ahead of Justin, then—

- Order of finish: Jordan, Justin, Jakob

If Joey crossed the finish line a dead heat with Jakob, then—

- Order of finish: Jordan, Justin, Jakob/Joey (tie)

If Josh was fifth at the finish, then everyone beat Josh—

- Order of finish: Jordan, Justin, Jakob/Joey (tie), Josh

Working Backward

Working backward is a good example of thinking differently.

Problem: Jonathan computed his average for five tests in his math class and found he had earned a 76. What must he score on the final two tests to raise his average to 80?

If Jonathan had 5 tests that averaged 76, his total number of points would be 5×76 or 380. Think about why that is true. Jonathan has two additional tests in which to bring up his average. He knows that to average 80 on all seven tests, he would need a total of 560 points ($80 \times 7 = 560$). Since Jonathan already has 380 points, he will need a total of 180 more points ($560 - 380 = 180$). Therefore, he needs to get scores of 90, or any combination with a sum of 180, on each of his two remaining tests. Do you think he can do it?

Drawing a Diagram

Drawing a Diagram can really help you visualize a problem, as you saw in the problems about the medicine tablets and fence poles.

Problem: How much will it cost to cut a log into 8 equal pieces, if you know that cutting it into 4 equal pieces costs 60 cents? Each piece must be cut separately. (*Hint: Think about the tablet and fence pole problems.*)

Cutting a log into 4 equal pieces will cost 60 cents. How much is that per cut? Fifteen cents? Think again.

Cut #	1	2	3

Since it takes only 3 cuts to create 4 equal pieces, the cost is 20 cents (60 cents ÷ 3 = 20 cents).

So, how much will it cost to cut the log into 8 equal pieces?

Cut #	1	2	3	4	5	6	7

Seven cuts at 20 cents each equals $1.40. Did you get it right?

How is this problem similar to the medicine tablet and fence pole problems? Can you see that each one appears to lead to an answer that is off by one item or unit each time? Do you find these problems are easier to understand when you draw a diagram? Even if you know the answer, drawing a diagram sometimes provides a great way to check your work.

Remember: Once the mathematical model has been solved, translating the result into a meaningful answer to the original equation is the crucial final step.

No Solution

Some problems don't have a solution!

Problem: Speedy drives 2 miles to work each morning. He must average 30 miles per hour to get to work on time. One morning, a slow driver gets in his way for the first mile, cutting his average to 15 mph. He tries to calculate the speed he'll need to drive for the rest of the trip to arrive on time. His car can go up to 120 mph. How fast must he drive the final mile?

Although this may seem like a somewhat complicated problem, it can be figured out in a number of ways. One of the simpler ways is to first figure out how long Speedy's trip normally takes. If he travels 2 miles each day at 30 mph, the trip will normally take 4 minutes, according to the formula:

$$\text{rate} \times \text{time} = \text{distance}$$
$$rt = d$$
$$30t = 2$$
$$t = \frac{2}{30} = \frac{1}{15} \text{ of an hour and } \frac{1}{15} \text{ hrs} \times \frac{60 \text{ minutes}}{1 \text{ hour}} = \frac{60}{15} = 4 \text{ minutes}$$

Then figure out how much time the first mile takes on the day that the driver slows Speedy down to 15 mph:

$$rt = d$$
$$15t = 1$$
$$t = \frac{1}{15} \text{ of an hour}$$

You already know that $\frac{1}{15}$ of an hour is 4 minutes, so there is no amount of speed that will get him to work on time. The first mile used all 4 minutes Speedy had allowed himself to get to work. His car could go 1000 mph, and Speedy would still be late.

Can you think of other ways to approach this problem?

Now that you have some effective strategies in mind, you can apply what you have learned to the five-step Plan for Solving a Word Problem.

Plan for Solving a Word Problem

Step 1 Read the problem carefully. Decide what unknown numbers are asked for and what facts are known. Making a sketch may help (or using one of the other strategies you have now learned).

Step 2 Choose a variable and use it with the given facts to represent the unknowns described in the problem.

Step 3 Reread the problem and write an equation that represents relationships among the numbers in the problem.

Step 4 Solve the equation and find the unknowns asked for.

Step 5 Check your results with the words of the problem. Give the answer.

Why Learn Problem Solving?

You may ask, "Why not simply rely on technology to solve the problems?" It is true that computers and calculators can solve long, difficult, monotonous problems, but only if they are given proper information and told exactly what to do. In other words, if you ask a computer for an answer, the answer will be only as correct as the instructions and facts you supply. Computer programmers sometimes use a term for what happens when the instructions and information given to a computer are wrong: "garbage in, garbage out." Calculators and computers know nothing more than what they are told, and they follow directions very well—both good directions and bad ones.

Problems without words are just numbers to be manipulated or equations to be solved. Do you know of any job where a person is paid to sit and just crunch numbers? We have wonderful technology to do that. Employers want men and women who can think critically, problem solve, dream, and invent. Develop your mind to think and work in different ways. Dare to be a visionary. The world is begging for people who can do these things. Are you willing to work to become one of them?

Five Characteristics of a Great Problem Solver

1. FLUENCY – The ability to find different ways to solve problems. Is there more than one answer? How many different approaches can you use?

2. FLEXIBILITY – The ability to look at a problem in a different way. Watch and listen to how others approach problems and learn from them. It is easy to think that everybody thinks just as you do, but it is not true. Collect a toolbox of different strategies to solve problems.

3. ORIGINALITY – The ability to think of a unique response. As you listen to others' ideas, you will learn different ways of thinking.

4. APPLICABILITY – The ability to elaborate on a problem by rephrasing it and using prior knowledge.

5. DILIGENCE/DRIVE – The ability to stick with a problem through mistakes, incorrect attempts, and "getting stuck" to finally solve it. Success and invention often come after a series of mistakes and false assumptions. The only time a mistake is a problem is when it is your last attempt. Do not give up!

Use the checklist below to help you develop your problem-solving skills! You may want to print multiple copies of this page to use throughout the course while solving problems.

In this guide, you have explored a number of problem-solving strategies, received a variety of tips for success, and reviewed the five-step Plan for Solving a Word Problem.

Below is a helpful checklist to bring all the information together that you've learned to help you develop into a great problem solver. As you use the checklist to remind yourself of how to approach problems, your problem-solving skills will improve not only in this course but also in all aspects of study.

Prior to solving the problem:

☐ Read the problem more than once.

☐ Be sure you understand what the problem says.

☐ Restate the problem in your own words.

☐ Try to remember a similar problem you have worked.

☐ Identify the information that directly applies to solving this problem.

☐ Disregard information you don't need.

As you solve the problem:

☐ Think about the steps required to solve the problem.

☐ Check your work as you go.

☐ Stop and rethink your steps.

Try different strategies:

☐ Experiment and simulate.

☐ Simplify and reduce the problem.

☐ Recognize a pattern in the problem.

☐ Guess and check.

☐ Use logical deduction.

☐ Work the problem backward.

☐ Draw a picture.

☐ Apply your own unique strategies.

After solving the problem:

☐ Check to see that your calculations are correct.

☐ Ask yourself whether your answer is reasonable.

☐ Solve the problem another way and compare the solutions.

Most of all, enjoy the experience.

Student Guide

Multiple Transformations

Life often involves dealing with a sequence of problems or challenges, and you can spend a lot of time deciding what to do next, figuring out how to get it done, and then doing it. Practice your problem-solving skills on word problems. As you become more expert at solving problems, you may find that your skills as a problem solver help you in many ways.

Goals for This Lesson
- Solve an equation involving more than one transformation.

- Solve a word problem that requires writing an equation with multiple transformations.

Graded Activities in This Lesson
Lesson Quiz (computer-scored)

Materials
Intermediate Mathematics C: A Reference Guide and Problem Sets, pages 58–62.

Optional
A Guide to Problem Solving
calculator

Keywords
inverse operations: mathematical operations that undo each other, such as addition and subtraction or multiplication and division

transformations: operations performed on an equation or an inequality that produce a simpler, equivalent equation

Groundwork: Preparing for the Lesson [online]
Take this time to review using inverse operations to solve equations and using equations to solve real-world problems.

Learn: Combining Transformations [online]

In this activity, you will learn how to solve equations using multiple transformations.

Use algebra tiles to solve $2x + 4 = 6$.

Directions for using the Algebra Tiles Learning Tool:

1. Enter the left side of the equation in the left expression box.

2. Enter the right side of the equation in the right expression box.

3. Select Build.

4. Add positive or negative tiles to the left and/or right side of the equation by dragging them from the box on the right side of the screen. Your goal is to have only x tiles on one side of the equals sign, and only unit tiles on the other side. Pay close attention to the equals sign. If it changes to a not equal sign, then the equation is out of balance. You must keep it in balance.

5. Look at how the equation changed. Write down the new equation.

6. When there are only x tiles on one side of the equation, select the division symbol button to create one row for each multiple of x. For example, for 2x, you need two rows.

7. Drag one of the x tile to each new row in the left column of the table so that there is one tile in each row.

8. Drag unit tiles to the new rows in the right column of the table. Only add tiles to rows where there are corresponding x tiles. Divide the unit tiles equally among these rows.

9. If the coefficient of x is negative, select Multiply by -1.

10. Look at one of the equal rows to see what 1x equals. Enter your answer and select Check.

Summarize what you learned in this activity.

Use the space provided here to record the important points presented in the animation.

Following the animation presented online, solve the following equations.

1. $2x + 3 = 9$.

2. $\dfrac{x}{9} - 5 = 3$

Worked Examples: Try Multiple Transformations [online]

Use the space below to work through the examples you see in the online screens.

Learn: Equations Are Key [online]

Use equations that require multiple transformations to solve word problems.

Use the spaces below to take notes during this activity.

Use the problem-solving plan to work through this problem.

A quilter needs a triangular section that has a total perimeter of 14 in. Two of the triangle's sides need to be 1 in. longer than the third side. How long is each side?

Identify.

Strategize.

Set Up.

Solve.

Check.

Worked Examples: Try Problems with Multiple Transformations

[online]
Use the space below to work through the examples you see in the online screens.

Summary: Multiple Transformations [online]

In this lesson, you learned how to use multiple transformations to solve equations.

When solving an equation where two or more transformations are needed, undo or reverse the order of operations.

Before using transformations, simplify the equation as much as possible.

The five-step method is an effective way to solve word problems with multiple transformations.

Step 1. **Identify**: Identify the unknown(s).

Step 2. **Strategize**: Choose a variable for the unknown.

Step 3. **Set Up**: Reread the problem and write an equation.

Step 4. **Solve**: Solve the equation and find the unknowns.

Step 5. **Check**: Check your answer if time permits.

Offline Learning: Multiple Transformations [offline]

Read pages 58–61.

Do the Math

You first learned to use transformations to solve equations involving only addition or subtraction. Then you used transformations to solve equations involving only multiplication or division. Now you will combine transformations to solve more complicated equations.

You can approach the solution of these equations in several different ways and get the same result. A few tips may help you decide what to do first and give you greater success in finding a solution set.

1. If needed, simplify one or both sides of the equation. This may involve combining like terms or eliminating a fractional representation.

2. When both sides are simplified, concentrate on the side containing the variable. If that side involves more than one operation, apply inverse operations just as you have been doing in the examples in this lesson.

   For example, if the side of the equation with the variable involves multiplication and addition, the typical order of operations is multiplication first and addition second. To undo the equation with inverse operations, first subtract to undo the addition and then divide (or multiply by the reciprocal) to undo the multiplication.

Often there is more than one way to solve an equation. You can decide which way is best after you have looked at the equation. Using the experience you are gaining now, look for reasons to choose a particular beginning step.

Solve. $\frac{1}{2}x + 7 = 6$

Strategy

No simplification is needed. The left side of the equation contains the variable. Two inverse operations are needed to solve the equation.

Solution

(1)	$\frac{1}{2}x + 7 = 6$	Original equation
(2)	$\frac{1}{2}x + 7 - 7 = 6 - 7$	Subtract 7 from each side.
(3)	$\frac{1}{2}x = -1$	Simplify.
(4)	$2\left(\frac{1}{2}\right)x = 2 \cdot -1$	Divide each side by $\frac{1}{2}$ (or multiply by 2).
(5)	$x = -2$	Simplify.

The solution set is {−2}.

Tips

- In the condensed solution, Steps 2 and 4 would be omitted.

Think About It *Why is simplification done on only one side of an equation at a time, while inverse operations are done on both sides of the equation at the same time?*

Try this next example to see how simplification may be necessary before using inverse operations.

Solve: $15 = 8x - 5 + 2x$

Strategy

Simplify the right side of the equation. Then use two inverse operations—addition and division—to solve the equation.

Solution

(1)	$15 = 8x - 5 + 2x$	Original equation
(2)	$15 = 10x - 5$	Simplify the right side of the equation: $8x + 2x$ is replaced with 10x.
(3)	$15 + 5 = 10x - 5 + 5$	Add 5 to each side.
(4)	$20 = 10x$	Simplify.
(5)	$\dfrac{20}{10} = \dfrac{10}{10}x$	Divide each side by 10.
(6)	$2 = x$	Simplify.

The solution set is {2}.

Tips

- In the condensed solution, Steps 3 and 5 would be omitted.

Remember: You have learned how important the Check step is to ensure that you have found the correct solution set. Even if you do not see the Check step written in the examples, always remember to replace the variable in the original equation with the solution and, either mentally or in writing, check it out for accuracy.

Answer to Think About It: Think of a set of balance scales. Getting the two sides to balance at the same level is the key. When simplifying an expression on one side of the equation, you are merely substituting an expression or term of equal value for one that is already there. So the balance of the equation is not affected.

However, when you add, subtract, multiply, or divide only one side of an equation by a value that is not an identity for an operation, the equation becomes unbalanced. To maintain balance, you must perform the same operation with the same value on both sides of the equation. Keeping a picture of a balance scale in mind should help you keep the ideas straight.

Problem Sets
Complete Problems 1–21 odd and 25–29 odd on pages 61–62.

Extension (optional)
Complete Problems 2–20 even and 24–28 even on pages 61–62.

Lesson Assessment: Multiple Transformations Quiz [online]
Now go back online to complete the Lesson Quiz.

Name _____   Date _____

A Guide to Problem Solving

Do you know people who seem to solve math problems with little effort? Perhaps you are one of those people.

Few problems in the real world, however, are in the form of an equation you just solve. In fact, the easiest part of solving a problem might be the last part—solving the equation. The key is learning where to start when you don't know how to set up an equation.

Remember: When solving a problem, writing the correct equation is at least as important as performing the calculations correctly.

As you gain more experience in problem solving, you will recognize that many problems are similar to each other. The strategies that you use to solve one problem will be useful in solving another, if they are the same type of problem. Below are examples of strategies that can be used.

You don't need to memorize the word problems presented here or the names of the strategies, but it is important that you recognize their characteristics. When you see similar problems later, you can draw upon this information to help you.

Experimentation and Simulation

Problem 1: A doctor gave Mr. Ache 8 tablets and instructed him to take one every 3 hours, starting immediately in the doctor's office. If Mr. Ache does as he is told, how long will it be until he has taken all of the tablets?

The apparent answer is 24 hours, but is that correct? By simulating the problem with a diagram, you can check your answer.

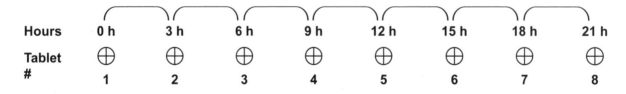

Hours	0 h	3 h	6 h	9 h	12 h	15 h	18 h	21 h
Tablet #	⊕ 1	⊕ 2	⊕ 3	⊕ 4	⊕ 5	⊕ 6	⊕ 7	⊕ 8

Count up the hours. The correct answer is 21 hours, not 24 hours. Mr. Ache takes the first tablet and *then* starts the 3-hour intervals.

You can also simulate this problem with candy pieces, eating one every 3 minutes starting now and timing the experiment from start to finish. (You might find that solving problems can be more fun than you thought!)

Problem 2: You are to erect a fence 100 feet long, placing the fence poles 10 feet apart. How many poles will you need to complete the task?

The apparent answer is 10, but is that correct? You can create a diagram to find out.

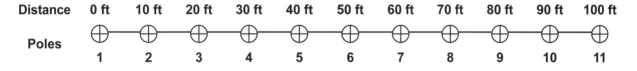

Distance	0 ft	10 ft	20 ft	30 ft	40 ft	50 ft	60 ft	70 ft	80 ft	90 ft	100 ft
Poles	1	2	3	4	5	6	7	8	9	10	11

You can see from the diagram that you will need 11 poles to complete this task, not 10.

Compare and contrast this fence pole problem and the tablet problem above. Can you see that knowing how to solve one of them can help you more easily solve the other and any future problems similar to these?

Computers and calculators can assist greatly with experimentation and simulation models. Now think about whether a computer could solve a problem, even a simple one like the two examples, without being given information in a language and form that it can process. Can you see how important it is to set up a problem correctly before attempting to solve it?

Remember: You can solve problems by identifying relationships, distinguishing between relevant and irrelevant information, identifying missing information, sequencing and prioritizing information, and observing patterns.

Simplification and Reduction

Problem: Big Bowl stadium seats 100,000 people. At the game, ushers estimate that there are 3 males seated for every 2 females in the sold-out stadium. How many males and how many females are in Big Bowl?

You know that—

	Males	Females
Rate	3 out of every 5 people are male	2 out of every 5 people are female
Multiply by 2	6 out of every 10 people are male	4 out of every 10 people are female
Multiply by 10	60 out of every 100 people are male	40 out of every 100 people are female

Because percent is an amount per 100, you now know that—

- 60% of 100,000 people or 60,000 people are male.
- 40% of 100,000 people or 40,000 people are female.

Pattern Recognition

Problem: Jason is having a party. The first time the doorbell rings, one guest enters. At each additional ring of the doorbell, a group enters that has two more people than the previous group had. How many total guests will have entered after the 18th ring?

A great way to discover patterns is to make a table, as follows:

Doorbell Ring	# Of Guests Arriving	Total # Of Guests
1	1	1
2	3	4
3	5	9
4	7	16
5	9	25
6	11	36
.	.	.
.	.	.
.	.	.

Do you notice a pattern? If so, you can go directly to the answer, rather than continuing with the table until you reach the 18th ring.

Compare the number of doorbell rings (first column) to the total number of guests who have arrived by that ring (third column). If r **equals** the number of doorbell rings, then—

r^2 = total number of guests who have arrived

Check it out!

So, the total number of guests after the 18th ring would be 18^2, which equals 324. Therefore, 324 guests will have arrived after 18 rings of the doorbell.

Remember: A problem may contain extra information that is not important to finding a solution. Identifying the necessary information in a problem is very important.

Guess and Test

Another strategy is the guess-and-test approach. You may be able to solve the next problem using mental math, with no pencil or paper required.

Problem: The Dubuque Dodgers and the Davenport Divers set a new semi-pro basketball league record last week when they scored 222 points between them in one game. If the Divers lost by 14 points, how many points did the Dodgers score?

One strategy in solving this problem is to just start guessing and try to come up with two scores that are separated by 14 points. If you stop to think for a minute, you will realize that out of 222 points, a difference of 14 points is not very much. The answer must be somewhere around one-half of 222. Using mental math, you can determine that 111 is the mean score. So, if you add and subtract 7 points to the mean score, you will see that the Dodgers scored 118 points (111 + 7 = 118) while the Divers scored 104 points (111 − 7 = 104 and 104 + 118 = 222). Great game!

Logical Deduction

Logical Deduction is a valuable strategy. Although the problem that follows is more like a puzzle, the type of thinking required to solve it is one you will use and apply your entire life.

Problem: Justin, Jakob, Josh, Joey, and Jordan were the first five finishers of a 16-mile race. From the given clues, give the order in which they finished.

1. Justin passed Jakob just before the finish line.
2. Jordan finished 10 seconds ahead of Justin.
3. Joey crossed the finish line in a dead heat with Jakob.
4. Josh was fifth at the finish.

Do you know where to begin? Consider each fact in the order it is written.

If Justin passed Jakob just before the finish line, then Justin finished before Jakob.

- Order of finish: Justin, Jakob

If Jordan finished 10 seconds ahead of Justin, then—

- Order of finish: Jordan, Justin, Jakob

If Joey crossed the finish line a dead heat with Jakob, then—

- Order of finish: Jordan, Justin, Jakob/Joey (tie)

If Josh was fifth at the finish, then everyone beat Josh—

- Order of finish: Jordan, Justin, Jakob/Joey (tie), Josh

Working Backward

Working backward is a good example of thinking differently.

Problem: Jonathan computed his average for five tests in his math class and found he had earned a 76. What must he score on the final two tests to raise his average to 80?

If Jonathan had 5 tests that averaged 76, his total number of points would be 5×76 or 380. Think about why that is true. Jonathan has two additional tests in which to bring up his average. He knows that to average 80 on all seven tests, he would need a total of 560 points ($80 \times 7 = 560$). Since Jonathan already has 380 points, he will need a total of 180 more points ($560 - 380 = 180$). Therefore, he needs to get scores of 90, or any combination with a sum of 180, on each of his two remaining tests. Do you think he can do it?

Drawing a Diagram

Drawing a Diagram can really help you visualize a problem, as you saw in the problems about the medicine tablets and fence poles.

Problem: How much will it cost to cut a log into 8 equal pieces, if you know that cutting it into 4 equal pieces costs 60 cents? Each piece must be cut separately. (*Hint: Think about the tablet and fence pole problems.*)

Cutting a log into 4 equal pieces will cost 60 cents. How much is that per cut? Fifteen cents? Think again.

Cut #	1	2	3

Since it takes only 3 cuts to create 4 equal pieces, the cost is 20 cents (60 cents ÷ 3 = 20 cents).

So, how much will it cost to cut the log into 8 equal pieces?

Cut #	1	2	3	4	5	6	7

Seven cuts at 20 cents each equals $1.40. Did you get it right?

How is this problem similar to the medicine tablet and fence pole problems? Can you see that each one appears to lead to an answer that is off by one item or unit each time? Do you find these problems are easier to understand when you draw a diagram? Even if you know the answer, drawing a diagram sometimes provides a great way to check your work.

Remember: Once the mathematical model has been solved, translating the result into a meaningful answer to the original equation is the crucial final step.

No Solution

Some problems don't have a solution!

Problem: Speedy drives 2 miles to work each morning. He must average 30 miles per hour to get to work on time. One morning, a slow driver gets in his way for the first mile, cutting his average to 15 mph. He tries to calculate the speed he'll need to drive for the rest of the trip to arrive on time. His car can go up to 120 mph. How fast must he drive the final mile?

Although this may seem like a somewhat complicated problem, it can be figured out in a number of ways. One of the simpler ways is to first figure out how long Speedy's trip normally takes. If he travels 2 miles each day at 30 mph, the trip will normally take 4 minutes, according to the formula:

$$\text{rate} \times \text{time} = \text{distance}$$
$$rt = d$$
$$30t = 2$$

$$t = \frac{2}{30} = \frac{1}{15} \text{ of an hour and } \frac{1}{15} \text{ hrs} \times \frac{60 \text{ minutes}}{1 \text{ hour}} = \frac{60}{15} = 4 \text{ minutes}$$

Then figure out how much time the first mile takes on the day that the driver slows Speedy down to 15 mph:

$$rt = d$$
$$15t = 1$$

$$t = \frac{1}{15} \text{ of an hour}$$

You already know that $\frac{1}{15}$ of an hour is 4 minutes, so there is no amount of speed that will get him to work on time. The first mile used all 4 minutes Speedy had allowed himself to get to work. His car could go 1000 mph, and Speedy would still be late.

Can you think of other ways to approach this problem?

Now that you have some effective strategies in mind, you can apply what you have learned to the five-step Plan for Solving a Word Problem.

Plan for Solving a Word Problem

Step 1 Read the problem carefully. Decide what unknown numbers are asked for and what facts are known. Making a sketch may help (or using one of the other strategies you have now learned).

Step 2 Choose a variable and use it with the given facts to represent the unknowns described in the problem.

Step 3 Reread the problem and write an equation that represents relationships among the numbers in the problem.

Step 4 Solve the equation and find the unknowns asked for.

Step 5 Check your results with the words of the problem. Give the answer.

Why Learn Problem Solving?

You may ask, "Why not simply rely on technology to solve the problems?" It is true that computers and calculators can solve long, difficult, monotonous problems, but only if they are given proper information and told exactly what to do. In other words, if you ask a computer for an answer, the answer will be only as correct as the instructions and facts you supply. Computer programmers sometimes use a term for what happens when the instructions and information given to a computer are wrong: "garbage in, garbage out." Calculators and computers know nothing more than what they are told, and they follow directions very well—both good directions and bad ones.

Problems without words are just numbers to be manipulated or equations to be solved. Do you know of any job where a person is paid to sit and just crunch numbers? We have wonderful technology to do that. Employers want men and women who can think critically, problem solve, dream, and invent. Develop your mind to think and work in different ways. Dare to be a visionary. The world is begging for people who can do these things. Are you willing to work to become one of them?

Five Characteristics of a Great Problem Solver

1. FLUENCY – The ability to find different ways to solve problems. Is there more than one answer? How many different approaches can you use?

2. FLEXIBILITY – The ability to look at a problem in a different way. Watch and listen to how others approach problems and learn from them. It is easy to think that everybody thinks just as you do, but it is not true. Collect a toolbox of different strategies to solve problems.

3. ORIGINALITY – The ability to think of a unique response. As you listen to others' ideas, you will learn different ways of thinking.

4. APPLICABILITY – The ability to elaborate on a problem by rephrasing it and using prior knowledge.

5. DILIGENCE/DRIVE – The ability to stick with a problem through mistakes, incorrect attempts, and "getting stuck" to finally solve it. Success and invention often come after a series of mistakes and false assumptions. The only time a mistake is a problem is when it is your last attempt. Do not give up!

Use the checklist below to help you develop your problem-solving skills! You may want to print multiple copies of this page to use throughout the course while solving problems.

In this guide, you have explored a number of problem-solving strategies, received a variety of tips for success, and reviewed the five-step Plan for Solving a Word Problem.

Below is a helpful checklist to bring all the information together that you've learned to help you develop into a great problem solver. As you use the checklist to remind yourself of how to approach problems, your problem-solving skills will improve not only in this course but also in all aspects of study.

Prior to solving the problem:

☐ Read the problem more than once.

☐ Be sure you understand what the problem says.

☐ Restate the problem in your own words.

☐ Try to remember a similar problem you have worked.

☐ Identify the information that directly applies to solving this problem.

☐ Disregard information you don't need.

As you solve the problem:

☐ Think about the steps required to solve the problem.

☐ Check your work as you go.

☐ Stop and rethink your steps.

Try different strategies:

☐ Experiment and simulate.

☐ Simplify and reduce the problem.

☐ Recognize a pattern in the problem.

☐ Guess and check.

☐ Use logical deduction.

☐ Work the problem backward.

☐ Draw a picture.

☐ Apply your own unique strategies.

After solving the problem:

☐ Check to see that your calculations are correct.

☐ Ask yourself whether your answer is reasonable.

☐ Solve the problem another way and compare the solutions.

Most of all, enjoy the experience.

Student Guide

Variables on Both Sides of an Equation

As you encounter more challenging and varied types of algebraic equations, you'll notice that many of them include variable terms on both sides of the equals sign. Rest easy—your problem-solving plan remains the same. You will still combine like terms on each side of the equation, and then use transformations to isolate and gather the variable terms on just one side. In this lesson, you will use this strategy to solve word problems by using equations that have variables on both sides.

Goals for This Lesson

* Solve an equation that has a variable on both sides.

* Solve word problems that involve equations with variables on both sides.

Graded Activities in This Lesson

Lesson Quiz (computer-scored)

Materials

Intermediate Mathematics C: A Reference Guide and Problem Sets, pages 63–66.

Optional

A Guide to Problem Solving
calculator

Keywords

empty set: the set with no elements, also known as the null set

inverse operations: mathematical operations that undo each other, such as addition and subtraction, or multiplication and division

solution (or root) of an equation: any value of a variable that turns an open sentence into a true statement

solution set of an equation: the set of all solutions of an equation

Groundwork: Preparing for the Lesson [online]

Take some time to review what you already know about solving equations.

Learn: Combine First [online]

So far, the equations you have solved have involved a variable on one side of the equals sign. Now you will learn how to solve equations that have a variable on both sides of the equals sign.

Solve: $2x - 1 = 4x + 3$

Directions for using the Algebra Tiles Learning Tool:

1. Enter the left side of the equation in the left expression box.

2. Enter the right side of the equation in the right expression box.

3. Select Build.

4. Add positive or negative x tiles and unit tiles to the left and/or right side of the equation by dragging them from the box on the right side of the screen. Your goal is to have only x tiles on one side of the equals sign and only unit tiles on the other side. Pay close attention to the equals sign. If it changes to a not-equal sign, then the equation is out of balance. You must keep it in balance.

5. Look at how the equation changes each time you add tiles. Write down the new equation.

6. When there are only x tiles on one side of the equation, select the division symbol to create one row for each multiple of x. For example, for $2x$, you need two row. to begin dividing. You will need to divide the tiles equally among the rows so that each row has only 1 x tile and an equal number of unit tiles.

7. Drag an x tile to each new row in the left column so that there is one tile in each row.

8. Drag unit tiles to the new rows in the right column of the table. Only add tiles to rows where there are corresponding x tiles. Divide the unit tiles equally among these rows.

9. If the coefficient of x is negative, select the (−1) button to multiply both sides of the equation by −1.

10. Enter your answer and select Check.

Answer the questions related to the algebra tile activity.

1. What did you do to get all of the x tiles on one side of the equation $2x - 1 = 4x + 3$?

2. Write the complete algebraic solution to the equation $2x - 1 = 4x + 3$.

Summarize what you learned in this activity.

1. What are the different types of solutions you can get when you solve equations variables on both sides?
2. Solve the equations.

$$4x + 6 = 2(2x + 3)$$

$$\frac{2x - 1}{2} = x + 5$$

3. Translate the word sentence into an equation, and then solve.

   Seven more than three times a number equals one more than five times the number.

   Write out the steps to solve the equation $3n = 64 - 5n$.

Worked Examples: Try Variables on Both Sides of an Equation

[online]
Use the space below to work through the examples you see in the online screens.

MathCast: Variables on Both Sides [online]
View the video to see how to solve a typical problem.

Summary: Variables on Both Sides of an Equation [online]

When there are variable terms on both sides of an equation, combine like terms on both sides first and then use transformations to simplify. Gather all the variable terms of an equation on one side. Then solve the equation.

When solving word problems, you now have a new tool to use: grouping all the variables on one side of the resulting equation.

Offline Learning: Variables on Both Sides of an Equation [offline]
Read pages 63–65.

Do the Math
Tips for Solving Equations with a Variable on Both Sides

- Simplify one or both sides of the equation as needed. This may involve applying the distributive property, combining like terms, or eliminating a fractional representation.

- When both sides have been simplified, concentrate on the positions of the variables. Although you can use the inverse operation to eliminate the variable on either side you choose, you may find that being selective about which side you choose can make the problem easier for you to solve.

  - If one side of the equation has a variable term and no constant term, you would want to eliminate the variable from the other side of the equation.

    Transform this term to isolate the
    variable on one side.

    $\downarrow$

    $8q = 5q - 24$

  - If there are both variable and numerical terms on both sides of the equation, you may want to choose which one to eliminate based on whether the result will give you a positive coefficient for the variable.

    Transform this term to get a positive
    coefficient for the variable.

    $\downarrow$

    $9 - 7m = 63 + 8m$

  - Develop your own preferences as you work through the problem sets.

- Once you have the variable on only one side, solve the equation as you have solved others in the past.

Problem Sets
Complete Problems 1–15 odd and 19–23 odd on pages 65–66.

Extension (optional)
Complete Problems 2–22 even on pages 65–66.

Lesson Assessment: Variables on Both Sides of an Equation Quiz

[online]
Now go back online to complete the Lesson Quiz.

Name _____   Date _____

A Guide to Problem Solving

Do you know people who seem to solve math problems with little effort? Perhaps you are one of those people.

Few problems in the real world, however, are in the form of an equation you just solve. In fact, the easiest part of solving a problem might be the last part—solving the equation. The key is learning where to start when you don't know how to set up an equation.

Remember: When solving a problem, writing the correct equation is at least as important as performing the calculations correctly.

As you gain more experience in problem solving, you will recognize that many problems are similar to each other. The strategies that you use to solve one problem will be useful in solving another, if they are the same type of problem. Below are examples of strategies that can be used.

You don't need to memorize the word problems presented here or the names of the strategies, but it is important that you recognize their characteristics. When you see similar problems later, you can draw upon this information to help you.

Experimentation and Simulation

Problem 1: A doctor gave Mr. Ache 8 tablets and instructed him to take one every 3 hours, starting immediately in the doctor's office. If Mr. Ache does as he is told, how long will it be until he has taken all of the tablets?

The apparent answer is 24 hours, but is that correct? By simulating the problem with a diagram, you can check your answer.

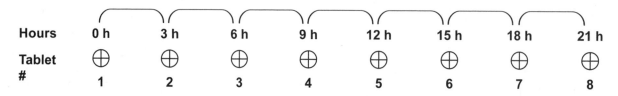

Hours	0 h	3 h	6 h	9 h	12 h	15 h	18 h	21 h
Tablet #	1	2	3	4	5	6	7	8

Count up the hours. The correct answer is 21 hours, not 24 hours. Mr. Ache takes the first tablet and *then* starts the 3-hour intervals.

You can also simulate this problem with candy pieces, eating one every 3 minutes starting now and timing the experiment from start to finish. (You might find that solving problems can be more fun than you thought!)

Problem 2: You are to erect a fence 100 feet long, placing the fence poles 10 feet apart. How many poles will you need to complete the task?

The apparent answer is 10, but is that correct? You can create a diagram to find out.

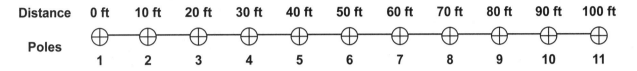

You can see from the diagram that you will need 11 poles to complete this task, not 10.

Compare and contrast this fence pole problem and the tablet problem above. Can you see that knowing how to solve one of them can help you more easily solve the other and any future problems similar to these?

Computers and calculators can assist greatly with experimentation and simulation models. Now think about whether a computer could solve a problem, even a simple one like the two examples, without being given information in a language and form that it can process. Can you see how important it is to set up a problem correctly before attempting to solve it?

Remember: You can solve problems by identifying relationships, distinguishing between relevant and irrelevant information, identifying missing information, sequencing and prioritizing information, and observing patterns.

Simplification and Reduction

Problem: Big Bowl stadium seats 100,000 people. At the game, ushers estimate that there are 3 males seated for every 2 females in the sold-out stadium. How many males and how many females are in Big Bowl?

You know that—

	Males	Females
Rate	3 out of every 5 people are male	2 out of every 5 people are female
Multiply by 2	6 out of every 10 people are male	4 out of every 10 people are female
Multiply by 10	60 out of every 100 people are male	40 out of every 100 people are female

Because percent is an amount per 100, you now know that—

* 60% of 100,000 people or 60,000 people are male.
* 40% of 100,000 people or 40,000 people are female.

Pattern Recognition

Problem: Jason is having a party. The first time the doorbell rings, one guest enters. At each additional ring of the doorbell, a group enters that has two more people than the previous group had. How many total guests will have entered after the 18th ring?

A great way to discover patterns is to make a table, as follows:

Doorbell Ring	# Of Guests Arriving	Total # Of Guests
1	1	1
2	3	4
3	5	9
4	7	16
5	9	25
6	11	36
.	.	.
.	.	.
.	.	.

Do you notice a pattern? If so, you can go directly to the answer, rather than continuing with the table until you reach the 18th ring.

Compare the number of doorbell rings (first column) to the total number of guests who have arrived by that ring (third column). If r **equals** the number of doorbell rings, then—

r^2 = total number of guests who have arrived

Check it out!

So, the total number of guests after the 18th ring would be 18^2, which equals 324. Therefore, 324 guests will have arrived after 18 rings of the doorbell.

Remember: A problem may contain extra information that is not important to finding a solution. Identifying the necessary information in a problem is very important.

Guess and Test

Another strategy is the guess-and-test approach. You may be able to solve the next problem using mental math, with no pencil or paper required.

Problem: The Dubuque Dodgers and the Davenport Divers set a new semi-pro basketball league record last week when they scored 222 points between them in one game. If the Divers lost by 14 points, how many points did the Dodgers score?

One strategy in solving this problem is to just start guessing and try to come up with two scores that are separated by 14 points. If you stop to think for a minute, you will realize that out of 222 points, a difference of 14 points is not very much. The answer must be somewhere around one-half of 222. Using mental math, you can determine that 111 is the mean score. So, if you add and subtract 7 points to the mean score, you will see that the Dodgers scored 118 points ($111 + 7 = 118$) while the Divers scored 104 points ($111 - 7 = 104$ and $104 + 118 = 222$). Great game!

Logical Deduction

Logical Deduction is a valuable strategy. Although the problem that follows is more like a puzzle, the type of thinking required to solve it is one you will use and apply your entire life.

Problem: Justin, Jakob, Josh, Joey, and Jordan were the first five finishers of a 16-mile race. From the given clues, give the order in which they finished.

1. Justin passed Jakob just before the finish line.

2. Jordan finished 10 seconds ahead of Justin.

3. Joey crossed the finish line in a dead heat with Jakob.

4. Josh was fifth at the finish.

Do you know where to begin? Consider each fact in the order it is written.

If Justin passed Jakob just before the finish line, then Justin finished before Jakob.

• Order of finish: Justin, Jakob

If Jordan finished 10 seconds ahead of Justin, then—

• Order of finish: Jordan, Justin, Jakob

If Joey crossed the finish line a dead heat with Jakob, then—

• Order of finish: Jordan, Justin, Jakob/Joey (tie)

If Josh was fifth at the finish, then everyone beat Josh—

• Order of finish: Jordan, Justin, Jakob/Joey (tie), Josh

Working Backward

Working backward is a good example of thinking differently.

Problem: Jonathan computed his average for five tests in his math class and found he had earned a 76. What must he score on the final two tests to raise his average to 80?

If Jonathan had 5 tests that averaged 76, his total number of points would be 5×76 or 380. Think about why that is true. Jonathan has two additional tests in which to bring up his average. He knows that to average 80 on all seven tests, he would need a total of 560 points ($80 \times 7 = 560$). Since Jonathan already has 380 points, he will need a total of 180 more points ($560 - 380 = 180$). Therefore, he needs to get scores of 90, or any combination with a sum of 180, on each of his two remaining tests. Do you think he can do it?

Drawing a Diagram

Drawing a Diagram can really help you visualize a problem, as you saw in the problems about the medicine tablets and fence poles.

Problem: How much will it cost to cut a log into 8 equal pieces, if you know that cutting it into 4 equal pieces costs 60 cents? Each piece must be cut separately. (*Hint: Think about the tablet and fence pole problems.*)

Cutting a log into 4 equal pieces will cost 60 cents. How much is that per cut? Fifteen cents? Think again.

Cut #	1	2	3

Since it takes only 3 cuts to create 4 equal pieces, the cost is 20 cents (60 cents ÷ 3 = 20 cents).

So, how much will it cost to cut the log into 8 equal pieces?

Cut #	1	2	3	4	5	6	7

Seven cuts at 20 cents each equals $1.40. Did you get it right?

How is this problem similar to the medicine tablet and fence pole problems? Can you see that each one appears to lead to an answer that is off by one item or unit each time? Do you find these problems are easier to understand when you draw a diagram? Even if you know the answer, drawing a diagram sometimes provides a great way to check your work.

Remember: Once the mathematical model has been solved, translating the result into a meaningful answer to the original equation is the crucial final step.

No Solution

Some problems don't have a solution!

Problem: Speedy drives 2 miles to work each morning. He must average 30 miles per hour to get to work on time. One morning, a slow driver gets in his way for the first mile, cutting his average to 15 mph. He tries to calculate the speed he'll need to drive for the rest of the trip to arrive on time. His car can go up to 120 mph. How fast must he drive the final mile?

Although this may seem like a somewhat complicated problem, it can be figured out in a number of ways. One of the simpler ways is to first figure out how long Speedy's trip normally takes. If he travels 2 miles each day at 30 mph, the trip will normally take 4 minutes, according to the formula:

$$\text{rate} \times \text{time} = \text{distance}$$
$$rt = d$$
$$30t = 2$$
$$t = \frac{2}{30} = \frac{1}{15} \text{ of an hour and } \frac{1}{15} \text{ hrs} \times \frac{60 \text{ minutes}}{1 \text{ hour}} = \frac{60}{15} = 4 \text{ minutes}$$

Then figure out how much time the first mile takes on the day that the driver slows Speedy down to 15 mph:

$$rt = d$$
$$15t = 1$$
$$t = \frac{1}{15} \text{ of an hour}$$

You already know that $\frac{1}{15}$ of an hour is 4 minutes, so there is no amount of speed that will get him to work on time. The first mile used all 4 minutes Speedy had allowed himself to get to work. His car could go 1000 mph, and Speedy would still be late.

Can you think of other ways to approach this problem?

Now that you have some effective strategies in mind, you can apply what you have learned to the five-step Plan for Solving a Word Problem.

Plan for Solving a Word Problem

Step 1 Read the problem carefully. Decide what unknown numbers are asked for and what facts are known. Making a sketch may help (or using one of the other strategies you have now learned).

Step 2 Choose a variable and use it with the given facts to represent the unknowns described in the problem.

Step 3 Reread the problem and write an equation that represents relationships among the numbers in the problem.

Step 4 Solve the equation and find the unknowns asked for.

Step 5 Check your results with the words of the problem. Give the answer.

Why Learn Problem Solving?

You may ask, "Why not simply rely on technology to solve the problems?" It is true that computers and calculators can solve long, difficult, monotonous problems, but only if they are given proper information and told exactly what to do. In other words, if you ask a computer for an answer, the answer will be only as correct as the instructions and facts you supply. Computer programmers sometimes use a term for what happens when the instructions and information given to a computer are wrong: "garbage in, garbage out." Calculators and computers know nothing more than what they are told, and they follow directions very well—both good directions and bad ones.

Problems without words are just numbers to be manipulated or equations to be solved. Do you know of any job where a person is paid to sit and just crunch numbers? We have wonderful technology to do that. Employers want men and women who can think critically, problem solve, dream, and invent. Develop your mind to think and work in different ways. Dare to be a visionary. The world is begging for people who can do these things. Are you willing to work to become one of them?

Five Characteristics of a Great Problem Solver

1. FLUENCY – The ability to find different ways to solve problems. Is there more than one answer? How many different approaches can you use?

2. FLEXIBILITY – The ability to look at a problem in a different way. Watch and listen to how others approach problems and learn from them. It is easy to think that everybody thinks just as you do, but it is not true. Collect a toolbox of different strategies to solve problems.

3. ORIGINALITY – The ability to think of a unique response. As you listen to others' ideas, you will learn different ways of thinking.

4. APPLICABILITY – The ability to elaborate on a problem by rephrasing it and using prior knowledge.

5. DILIGENCE/DRIVE – The ability to stick with a problem through mistakes, incorrect attempts, and "getting stuck" to finally solve it. Success and invention often come after a series of mistakes and false assumptions. The only time a mistake is a problem is when it is your last attempt. Do not give up!

Use the checklist below to help you develop your problem-solving skills! You may want to print multiple copies of this page to use throughout the course while solving problems.

In this guide, you have explored a number of problem-solving strategies, received a variety of tips for success, and reviewed the five-step Plan for Solving a Word Problem.

Below is a helpful checklist to bring all the information together that you've learned to help you develop into a great problem solver. As you use the checklist to remind yourself of how to approach problems, your problem-solving skills will improve not only in this course but also in all aspects of study.

Prior to solving the problem:

☐ Read the problem more than once.

☐ Be sure you understand what the problem says.

☐ Restate the problem in your own words.

☐ Try to remember a similar problem you have worked.

☐ Identify the information that directly applies to solving this problem.

☐ Disregard information you don't need.

As you solve the problem:

☐ Think about the steps required to solve the problem.

☐ Check your work as you go.

☐ Stop and rethink your steps.

Try different strategies:

☐ Experiment and simulate.

☐ Simplify and reduce the problem.

☐ Recognize a pattern in the problem.

☐ Guess and check.

☐ Use logical deduction.

☐ Work the problem backward.

☐ Draw a picture.

☐ Apply your own unique strategies.

After solving the problem:

☐ Check to see that your calculations are correct.

☐ Ask yourself whether your answer is reasonable.

☐ Solve the problem another way and compare the solutions.

Most of all, enjoy the experience.

Student Guide

Strange Solutions

You've solved equations with the variable on one side of the equals sign and with the variable on both sides of the equals sign. In both of these situations, the solution has been a single value for the variable. Do all equations have one solution? No. In fact, when the variable is on both sides of the equals sign, an equation could have no solution or infinitely many solutions. In this lesson, you will learn about these cases.

Goals for This Lesson
- Identify an equation as an identity, a contradiction, or neither.
- Determine whether given linear equations have one solution, no solution, or infinite solutions.
- Create equations that have one solution, no solution, or infinite solutions.

Graded Activities in This Lesson
Lesson Quiz (computer-scored)

Materials
Intermediate Mathematics C: A Reference Guide and Problem Sets, pages 67–70

Optional
A Guide to Problem Solving
calculator

Keywords
contradiction: an equation that is true for no values of the variable

identity: an equation that is true for any value of the variable

Learn: One Solution, No Solution, Infinite Solutions [online]
You will learn how to identify equations as identities, contradictions, or neither, and you will determine whether equations have one solution, no solution, or infinitely many solutions.

Summarize what you learned in this activity.

1. An equation has to be in _____ form before you can inspect it to determine whether it has one solution, no solution, or many solutions.

2. What indicates that an equation has one solution?

3. What indicates that an equation has no solution?

4. What indicates that an equation has infinitely many solutions?

5. What do you call an equation that has no solution?

6. What do you call an equation that has infinitely many solutions?

Worked Examples: One Solution, No Solution, Infinite Solutions [online]
Use the space below to work through the examples you see in the online screens.

Summary: Strange Solutions [online]

When solving an equation results in a true statement of a constant equal to itself, the equation is an identity and has an infinite number of solutions.

When solving an equation results in a false statement of a constant equal to another constant, the equation is a contradiction and has no solution.

You can determine whether an equation has one solution, infinitely many solutions, or no solution through inspection. First simplify both sides of the equation, and then compare the coefficients of the variable terms on both sides as well as the constant terms.

Offline Learning: Strange Solutions [offline]
Read pages 67–69.

Problem Sets
Complete Problems 1–9 and 11–16 on pages 69–70.

Lesson Assessment: Strange Solutions Quiz [online]
Go back online to complete the Lesson Quiz.

Name _____   Date _____

A Guide to Problem Solving

Do you know people who seem to solve math problems with little effort? Perhaps you are one of those people.

Few problems in the real world, however, are in the form of an equation you just solve. In fact, the easiest part of solving a problem might be the last part—solving the equation. The key is learning where to start when you don't know how to set up an equation.

Remember: When solving a problem, writing the correct equation is at least as important as performing the calculations correctly.

As you gain more experience in problem solving, you will recognize that many problems are similar to each other. The strategies that you use to solve one problem will be useful in solving another, if they are the same type of problem. Below are examples of strategies that can be used.

You don't need to memorize the word problems presented here or the names of the strategies, but it is important that you recognize their characteristics. When you see similar problems later, you can draw upon this information to help you.

Experimentation and Simulation

Problem 1: A doctor gave Mr. Ache 8 tablets and instructed him to take one every 3 hours, starting immediately in the doctor's office. If Mr. Ache does as he is told, how long will it be until he has taken all of the tablets?

The apparent answer is 24 hours, but is that correct? By simulating the problem with a diagram, you can check your answer.

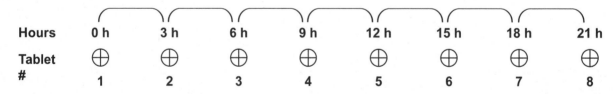

Hours	0 h	3 h	6 h	9 h	12 h	15 h	18 h	21 h
Tablet #	⊕ 1	⊕ 2	⊕ 3	⊕ 4	⊕ 5	⊕ 6	⊕ 7	⊕ 8

Count up the hours. The correct answer is 21 hours, not 24 hours. Mr. Ache takes the first tablet and *then* starts the 3-hour intervals.

You can also simulate this problem with candy pieces, eating one every 3 minutes starting now and timing the experiment from start to finish. (You might find that solving problems can be more fun than you thought!)

Problem 2: You are to erect a fence 100 feet long, placing the fence poles 10 feet apart. How many poles will you need to complete the task?

The apparent answer is 10, but is that correct? You can create a diagram to find out.

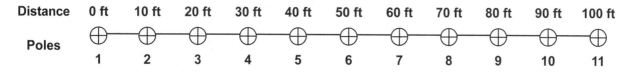

You can see from the diagram that you will need 11 poles to complete this task, not 10.

Compare and contrast this fence pole problem and the tablet problem above. Can you see that knowing how to solve one of them can help you more easily solve the other and any future problems similar to these?

Computers and calculators can assist greatly with experimentation and simulation models. Now think about whether a computer could solve a problem, even a simple one like the two examples, without being given information in a language and form that it can process. Can you see how important it is to set up a problem correctly before attempting to solve it?

Remember: You can solve problems by identifying relationships, distinguishing between relevant and irrelevant information, identifying missing information, sequencing and prioritizing information, and observing patterns.

Simplification and Reduction

Problem: Big Bowl stadium seats 100,000 people. At the game, ushers estimate that there are 3 males seated for every 2 females in the sold-out stadium. How many males and how many females are in Big Bowl?

You know that—

	Males	Females
Rate	3 out of every 5 people are male	2 out of every 5 people are female
Multiply by 2	6 out of every 10 people are male	4 out of every 10 people are female
Multiply by 10	60 out of every 100 people are male	40 out of every 100 people are female

Because percent is an amount per 100, you now know that—

- 60% of 100,000 people or 60,000 people are male.
- 40% of 100,000 people or 40,000 people are female.

Pattern Recognition

Problem: Jason is having a party. The first time the doorbell rings, one guest enters. At each additional ring of the doorbell, a group enters that has two more people than the previous group had. How many total guests will have entered after the 18th ring?

A great way to discover patterns is to make a table, as follows:

Doorbell Ring	# Of Guests Arriving	Total # Of Guests
1	1	1
2	3	4
3	5	9
4	7	16
5	9	25
6	11	36
.	.	.
.	.	.
.	.	.

Do you notice a pattern? If so, you can go directly to the answer, rather than continuing with the table until you reach the 18th ring.

Compare the number of doorbell rings (first column) to the total number of guests who have arrived by that ring (third column). If r **equals** the number of doorbell rings, then—

r^2 = total number of guests who have arrived

Check it out!

So, the total number of guests after the 18th ring would be 18^2, which equals 324. Therefore, 324 guests will have arrived after 18 rings of the doorbell.

Remember: A problem may contain extra information that is not important to finding a solution. Identifying the necessary information in a problem is very important.

Guess and Test

Another strategy is the guess-and-test approach. You may be able to solve the next problem using mental math, with no pencil or paper required.

Problem: The Dubuque Dodgers and the Davenport Divers set a new semi-pro basketball league record last week when they scored 222 points between them in one game. If the Divers lost by 14 points, how many points did the Dodgers score?

One strategy in solving this problem is to just start guessing and try to come up with two scores that are separated by 14 points. If you stop to think for a minute, you will realize that out of 222 points, a difference of 14 points is not very much. The answer must be somewhere around one-half of 222. Using mental math, you can determine that 111 is the mean score. So, if you add and subtract 7 points to the mean score, you will see that the Dodgers scored 118 points (111 + 7 = 118) while the Divers scored 104 points (111 − 7 = 104 and 104 + 118 = 222). Great game!

Logical Deduction

Logical Deduction is a valuable strategy. Although the problem that follows is more like a puzzle, the type of thinking required to solve it is one you will use and apply your entire life.

Problem: Justin, Jakob, Josh, Joey, and Jordan were the first five finishers of a 16-mile race. From the given clues, give the order in which they finished.

1. Justin passed Jakob just before the finish line.
2. Jordan finished 10 seconds ahead of Justin.
3. Joey crossed the finish line in a dead heat with Jakob.
4. Josh was fifth at the finish.

Do you know where to begin? Consider each fact in the order it is written.

If Justin passed Jakob just before the finish line, then Justin finished before Jakob.

*   Order of finish: Justin, Jakob

If Jordan finished 10 seconds ahead of Justin, then—

*   Order of finish: Jordan, Justin, Jakob

If Joey crossed the finish line a dead heat with Jakob, then—

*   Order of finish: Jordan, Justin, Jakob/Joey (tie)

If Josh was fifth at the finish, then everyone beat Josh—

*   Order of finish: Jordan, Justin, Jakob/Joey (tie), Josh

Working Backward

Working backward is a good example of thinking differently.

Problem: Jonathan computed his average for five tests in his math class and found he had earned a 76. What must he score on the final two tests to raise his average to 80?

If Jonathan had 5 tests that averaged 76, his total number of points would be 5×76 or 380.
Think about why that is true. Jonathan has two additional tests in which to bring up his average.
He knows that to average 80 on all seven tests, he would need a total of 560 points ($80 \times 7 = 560$).
Since Jonathan already has 380 points, he will need a total of 180 more points ($560 - 380 = 180$).
Therefore, he needs to get scores of 90, or any combination with a sum of 180, on each of his two remaining tests. Do you think he can do it?

Drawing a Diagram

Drawing a Diagram can really help you visualize a problem, as you saw in the problems about the medicine tablets and fence poles.

Problem: How much will it cost to cut a log into 8 equal pieces, if you know that cutting it into 4 equal pieces costs 60 cents? Each piece must be cut separately. (*Hint: Think about the tablet and fence pole problems.*)

Cutting a log into 4 equal pieces will cost 60 cents. How much is that per cut? Fifteen cents? Think again.

Cut #	1	2	3

Since it takes only 3 cuts to create 4 equal pieces, the cost is 20 cents (60 cents ÷ 3 = 20 cents).

So, how much will it cost to cut the log into 8 equal pieces?

Cut #	1	2	3	4	5	6	7

Seven cuts at 20 cents each equals $1.40. Did you get it right?

How is this problem similar to the medicine tablet and fence pole problems? Can you see that each one appears to lead to an answer that is off by one item or unit each time? Do you find these problems are easier to understand when you draw a diagram? Even if you know the answer, drawing a diagram sometimes provides a great way to check your work.

Remember: Once the mathematical model has been solved, translating the result into a meaningful answer to the original equation is the crucial final step.

No Solution

Some problems don't have a solution!

Problem: Speedy drives 2 miles to work each morning. He must average 30 miles per hour to get to work on time. One morning, a slow driver gets in his way for the first mile, cutting his average to 15 mph. He tries to calculate the speed he'll need to drive for the rest of the trip to arrive on time. His car can go up to 120 mph. How fast must he drive the final mile?

Although this may seem like a somewhat complicated problem, it can be figured out in a number of ways. One of the simpler ways is to first figure out how long Speedy's trip normally takes. If he travels 2 miles each day at 30 mph, the trip will normally take 4 minutes, according to the formula:

$$\text{rate} \times \text{time} = \text{distance}$$
$$rt = d$$
$$30t = 2$$

$$t = \frac{2}{30} = \frac{1}{15} \text{ of an hour and } \frac{1}{15} \text{ hrs} \times \frac{60 \text{ minutes}}{1 \text{ hour}} = \frac{60}{15} = 4 \text{ minutes}$$

Then figure out how much time the first mile takes on the day that the driver slows Speedy down to 15 mph:

$$rt = d$$
$$15t = 1$$

$$t = \frac{1}{15} \text{ of an hour}$$

You already know that $\frac{1}{15}$ of an hour is 4 minutes, so there is no amount of speed that will get him to work on time. The first mile used all 4 minutes Speedy had allowed himself to get to work. His car could go 1000 mph, and Speedy would still be late.

Can you think of other ways to approach this problem?

Now that you have some effective strategies in mind, you can apply what you have learned to the five-step Plan for Solving a Word Problem.

Plan for Solving a Word Problem

Step 1 Read the problem carefully. Decide what unknown numbers are asked for and what facts are known. Making a sketch may help (or using one of the other strategies you have now learned).

Step 2 Choose a variable and use it with the given facts to represent the unknowns described in the problem.

Step 3 Reread the problem and write an equation that represents relationships among the numbers in the problem.

Step 4 Solve the equation and find the unknowns asked for.

Step 5 Check your results with the words of the problem. Give the answer.

Why Learn Problem Solving?

You may ask, "Why not simply rely on technology to solve the problems?" It is true that computers and calculators can solve long, difficult, monotonous problems, but only if they are given proper information and told exactly what to do. In other words, if you ask a computer for an answer, the answer will be only as correct as the instructions and facts you supply. Computer programmers sometimes use a term for what happens when the instructions and information given to a computer are wrong: "garbage in, garbage out." Calculators and computers know nothing more than what they are told, and they follow directions very well—both good directions and bad ones.

Problems without words are just numbers to be manipulated or equations to be solved. Do you know of any job where a person is paid to sit and just crunch numbers? We have wonderful technology to do that. Employers want men and women who can think critically, problem solve, dream, and invent. Develop your mind to think and work in different ways. Dare to be a visionary. The world is begging for people who can do these things. Are you willing to work to become one of them?

Five Characteristics of a Great Problem Solver

1. FLUENCY – The ability to find different ways to solve problems. Is there more than one answer? How many different approaches can you use?

2. FLEXIBILITY – The ability to look at a problem in a different way. Watch and listen to how others approach problems and learn from them. It is easy to think that everybody thinks just as you do, but it is not true. Collect a toolbox of different strategies to solve problems.

3. ORIGINALITY – The ability to think of a unique response. As you listen to others' ideas, you will learn different ways of thinking.

4. APPLICABILITY – The ability to elaborate on a problem by rephrasing it and using prior knowledge.

5. DILIGENCE/DRIVE – The ability to stick with a problem through mistakes, incorrect attempts, and "getting stuck" to finally solve it. Success and invention often come after a series of mistakes and false assumptions. The only time a mistake is a problem is when it is your last attempt. Do not give up!

Use the checklist below to help you develop your problem-solving skills! You may want to print multiple copies of this page to use throughout the course while solving problems.

In this guide, you have explored a number of problem-solving strategies, received a variety of tips for success, and reviewed the five-step Plan for Solving a Word Problem.

Below is a helpful checklist to bring all the information together that you've learned to help you develop into a great problem solver. As you use the checklist to remind yourself of how to approach problems, your problem-solving skills will improve not only in this course but also in all aspects of study.

Prior to solving the problem:

☐ Read the problem more than once.

☐ Be sure you understand what the problem says.

☐ Restate the problem in your own words.

☐ Try to remember a similar problem you have worked.

☐ Identify the information that directly applies to solving this problem.

☐ Disregard information you don't need.

As you solve the problem:

☐ Think about the steps required to solve the problem.

☐ Check your work as you go.

☐ Stop and rethink your steps.

Try different strategies:

☐ Experiment and simulate.

☐ Simplify and reduce the problem.

☐ Recognize a pattern in the problem.

☐ Guess and check.

☐ Use logical deduction.

☐ Work the problem backward.

☐ Draw a picture.

☐ Apply your own unique strategies.

After solving the problem:

☐ Check to see that your calculations are correct.

☐ Ask yourself whether your answer is reasonable.

☐ Solve the problem another way and compare the solutions.

Most of all, enjoy the experience.

Student Guide

Core Focus: Problem Solving with Equations

To solve everyday mathematical problems, it's important to follow a logical procedure to organize your work and your thinking. In this lesson, you will learn how to follow the five-step problem-solving plan to write and solve equations that model real-world problems.

Goals for This Lesson
- Write a variable expression for a word problem.
- Solve word problems that involve equations with variables on both sides.

Graded Activities in This Lesson
Lesson Quiz (computer-graded)

Materials
Intermediate Mathematics C: A Reference Guide and Problem Sets, pages 71–73

Optional
A Guide to Problem Solving

calculator

Groundwork: Find the Error [online]
You will find the error in the solution to a word problem.

Learn: Problem Solving with a Plan [online]
Use the space below to take notes during this activity.

Core Focus

Overview

Summary

Worked Examples: Problem Solving with a Plan [online]
Use the space below to work through the examples you see in the online screens.

Offline Learning: Core Focus: Problem Solving with Equations

[offline]
Read pages 71–72.

Problem Sets
Complete Problems 1–4 on pages 72–73.

Lesson Assessment: Core Focus: Problem Solving with Equations Quiz [online]
Go back online to complete the Lesson Quiz.

Name _____   Date _____

A Guide to Problem Solving

Do you know people who seem to solve math problems with little effort? Perhaps you are one of those people.

Few problems in the real world, however, are in the form of an equation you just solve. In fact, the easiest part of solving a problem might be the last part—solving the equation. The key is learning where to start when you don't know how to set up an equation.

Remember: When solving a problem, writing the correct equation is at least as important as performing the calculations correctly.

As you gain more experience in problem solving, you will recognize that many problems are similar to each other. The strategies that you use to solve one problem will be useful in solving another, if they are the same type of problem. Below are examples of strategies that can be used.

You don't need to memorize the word problems presented here or the names of the strategies, but it is important that you recognize their characteristics. When you see similar problems later, you can draw upon this information to help you.

Experimentation and Simulation

Problem 1: A doctor gave Mr. Ache 8 tablets and instructed him to take one every 3 hours, starting immediately in the doctor's office. If Mr. Ache does as he is told, how long will it be until he has taken all of the tablets?

The apparent answer is 24 hours, but is that correct? By simulating the problem with a diagram, you can check your answer.

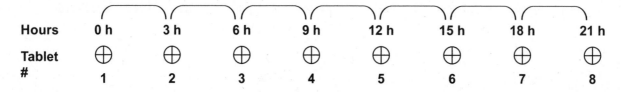

Hours	0 h	3 h	6 h	9 h	12 h	15 h	18 h	21 h
Tablet #	⊕ 1	⊕ 2	⊕ 3	⊕ 4	⊕ 5	⊕ 6	⊕ 7	⊕ 8

Count up the hours. The correct answer is 21 hours, not 24 hours. Mr. Ache takes the first tablet and *then* starts the 3-hour intervals.

You can also simulate this problem with candy pieces, eating one every 3 minutes starting now and timing the experiment from start to finish. (You might find that solving problems can be more fun than you thought!)

Problem 2: You are to erect a fence 100 feet long, placing the fence poles 10 feet apart. How many poles will you need to complete the task?

The apparent answer is 10, but is that correct? You can create a diagram to find out.

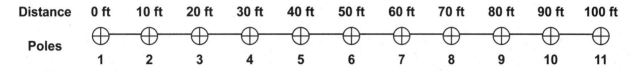

You can see from the diagram that you will need 11 poles to complete this task, not 10.

Compare and contrast this fence pole problem and the tablet problem above. Can you see that knowing how to solve one of them can help you more easily solve the other and any future problems similar to these?

Computers and calculators can assist greatly with experimentation and simulation models. Now think about whether a computer could solve a problem, even a simple one like the two examples, without being given information in a language and form that it can process. Can you see how important it is to set up a problem correctly before attempting to solve it?

Remember: You can solve problems by identifying relationships, distinguishing between relevant and irrelevant information, identifying missing information, sequencing and prioritizing information, and observing patterns.

Simplification and Reduction

Problem: Big Bowl stadium seats 100,000 people. At the game, ushers estimate that there are 3 males seated for every 2 females in the sold-out stadium. How many males and how many females are in Big Bowl?

You know that—

	Males	Females
Rate	3 out of every 5 people are male	2 out of every 5 people are female
Multiply by 2	6 out of every 10 people are male	4 out of every 10 people are female
Multiply by 10	60 out of every 100 people are male	40 out of every 100 people are female

Because percent is an amount per 100, you now know that—

* 60% of 100,000 people or 60,000 people are male.
* 40% of 100,000 people or 40,000 people are female.

Pattern Recognition

Problem: Jason is having a party. The first time the doorbell rings, one guest enters. At each additional ring of the doorbell, a group enters that has two more people than the previous group had. How many total guests will have entered after the 18th ring?

A great way to discover patterns is to make a table, as follows:

Doorbell Ring	# Of Guests Arriving	Total # Of Guests
1	1	1
2	3	4
3	5	9
4	7	16
5	9	25
6	11	36
•	•	•
•	•	•
•	•	•

Do you notice a pattern? If so, you can go directly to the answer, rather than continuing with the table until you reach the 18th ring.

Compare the number of doorbell rings (first column) to the total number of guests who have arrived by that ring (third column). If *r* **equals** the number of doorbell rings, then—

r^2 = total number of guests who have arrived

Check it out!

So, the total number of guests after the 18th ring would be 18^2, which equals 324. Therefore, 324 guests will have arrived after 18 rings of the doorbell.

Remember: A problem may contain extra information that is not important to finding a solution. Identifying the necessary information in a problem is very important.

Guess and Test

Another strategy is the guess-and-test approach. You may be able to solve the next problem using mental math, with no pencil or paper required.

Problem: The Dubuque Dodgers and the Davenport Divers set a new semi-pro basketball league record last week when they scored 222 points between them in one game. If the Divers lost by 14 points, how many points did the Dodgers score?

One strategy in solving this problem is to just start guessing and try to come up with two scores that are separated by 14 points. If you stop to think for a minute, you will realize that out of 222 points, a difference of 14 points is not very much. The answer must be somewhere around one-half of 222. Using mental math, you can determine that 111 is the mean score. So, if you add and subtract 7 points to the mean score, you will see that the Dodgers scored 118 points ($111 + 7 = 118$) while the Divers scored 104 points ($111 - 7 = 104$ and $104 + 118 = 222$). Great game!

Logical Deduction

Logical Deduction is a valuable strategy. Although the problem that follows is more like a puzzle, the type of thinking required to solve it is one you will use and apply your entire life.

Problem: Justin, Jakob, Josh, Joey, and Jordan were the first five finishers of a 16-mile race. From the given clues, give the order in which they finished.

1.   Justin passed Jakob just before the finish line.

2.   Jordan finished 10 seconds ahead of Justin.

3.   Joey crossed the finish line in a dead heat with Jakob.

4.   Josh was fifth at the finish.

Do you know where to begin? Consider each fact in the order it is written.

If Justin passed Jakob just before the finish line, then Justin finished before Jakob.

- Order of finish: Justin, Jakob

If Jordan finished 10 seconds ahead of Justin, then—

- Order of finish: Jordan, Justin, Jakob

If Joey crossed the finish line a dead heat with Jakob, then—

- Order of finish: Jordan, Justin, Jakob/Joey (tie)

If Josh was fifth at the finish, then everyone beat Josh—

- Order of finish: Jordan, Justin, Jakob/Joey (tie), Josh

Working Backward

Working backward is a good example of thinking differently.

Problem: Jonathan computed his average for five tests in his math class and found he had earned a 76. What must he score on the final two tests to raise his average to 80?

If Jonathan had 5 tests that averaged 76, his total number of points would be 5×76 or 380.
Think about why that is true. Jonathan has two additional tests in which to bring up his average.
He knows that to average 80 on all seven tests, he would need a total of 560 points ($80 \times 7 = 560$).
Since Jonathan already has 380 points, he will need a total of 180 more points ($560 - 380 = 180$).
Therefore, he needs to get scores of 90, or any combination with a sum of 180, on each of his two remaining tests. Do you think he can do it?

Drawing a Diagram

Drawing a Diagram can really help you visualize a problem, as you saw in the problems about the medicine tablets and fence poles.

Problem: How much will it cost to cut a log into 8 equal pieces, if you know that cutting it into 4 equal pieces costs 60 cents? Each piece must be cut separately. (*Hint: Think about the tablet and fence pole problems.*)

Cutting a log into 4 equal pieces will cost 60 cents. How much is that per cut? Fifteen cents? Think again.

Cut #	1	2	3

Since it takes only 3 cuts to create 4 equal pieces, the cost is 20 cents (60 cents ÷ 3 = 20 cents).

So, how much will it cost to cut the log into 8 equal pieces?

Cut #	1	2	3	4	5	6	7

Seven cuts at 20 cents each equals $1.40. Did you get it right?

How is this problem similar to the medicine tablet and fence pole problems? Can you see that each one appears to lead to an answer that is off by one item or unit each time? Do you find these problems are easier to understand when you draw a diagram? Even if you know the answer, drawing a diagram sometimes provides a great way to check your work.

Remember: Once the mathematical model has been solved, translating the result into a meaningful answer to the original equation is the crucial final step.

No Solution

Some problems don't have a solution!

Problem: Speedy drives 2 miles to work each morning. He must average 30 miles per hour to get to work on time. One morning, a slow driver gets in his way for the first mile, cutting his average to 15 mph. He tries to calculate the speed he'll need to drive for the rest of the trip to arrive on time. His car can go up to 120 mph. How fast must he drive the final mile?

Although this may seem like a somewhat complicated problem, it can be figured out in a number of ways. One of the simpler ways is to first figure out how long Speedy's trip normally takes. If he travels 2 miles each day at 30 mph, the trip will normally take 4 minutes, according to the formula:

$$\text{rate} \times \text{time} = \text{distance}$$
$$rt = d$$
$$30t = 2$$
$$t = \frac{2}{30} = \frac{1}{15} \text{ of an hour and } \frac{1}{15} \text{ hrs} \times \frac{60 \text{ minutes}}{1 \text{ hour}} = \frac{60}{15} = 4 \text{ minutes}$$

Then figure out how much time the first mile takes on the day that the driver slows Speedy down to 15 mph:

$$rt = d$$
$$15t = 1$$
$$t = \frac{1}{15} \text{ of an hour}$$

You already know that $\frac{1}{15}$ of an hour is 4 minutes, so there is no amount of speed that will get him to work on time. The first mile used all 4 minutes Speedy had allowed himself to get to work. His car could go 1000 mph, and Speedy would still be late.

Can you think of other ways to approach this problem?

> Now that you have some effective strategies in mind, you can apply what you have learned to the five-step Plan for Solving a Word Problem.
>
> ## Plan for Solving a Word Problem
>
> **Step 1** Read the problem carefully. Decide what unknown numbers are asked for and what facts are known. Making a sketch may help (or using one of the other strategies you have now learned).
>
> **Step 2** Choose a variable and use it with the given facts to represent the unknowns described in the problem.
>
> **Step 3** Reread the problem and write an equation that represents relationships among the numbers in the problem.
>
> **Step 4** Solve the equation and find the unknowns asked for.
>
> **Step 5** Check your results with the words of the problem. Give the answer.

Why Learn Problem Solving?

You may ask, "Why not simply rely on technology to solve the problems?" It is true that computers and calculators can solve long, difficult, monotonous problems, but only if they are given proper information and told exactly what to do. In other words, if you ask a computer for an answer, the answer will be only as correct as the instructions and facts you supply. Computer programmers sometimes use a term for what happens when the instructions and information given to a computer are wrong: "garbage in, garbage out." Calculators and computers know nothing more than what they are told, and they follow directions very well—both good directions and bad ones.

Problems without words are just numbers to be manipulated or equations to be solved. Do you know of any job where a person is paid to sit and just crunch numbers? We have wonderful technology to do that. Employers want men and women who can think critically, problem solve, dream, and invent. Develop your mind to think and work in different ways. Dare to be a visionary. The world is begging for people who can do these things. Are you willing to work to become one of them?

Five Characteristics of a Great Problem Solver

1. FLUENCY – The ability to find different ways to solve problems. Is there more than one answer? How many different approaches can you use?

2. FLEXIBILITY – The ability to look at a problem in a different way. Watch and listen to how others approach problems and learn from them. It is easy to think that everybody thinks just as you do, but it is not true. Collect a toolbox of different strategies to solve problems.

3. ORIGINALITY – The ability to think of a unique response. As you listen to others' ideas, you will learn different ways of thinking.

4. APPLICABILITY – The ability to elaborate on a problem by rephrasing it and using prior knowledge.

5. DILIGENCE/DRIVE – The ability to stick with a problem through mistakes, incorrect attempts, and "getting stuck" to finally solve it. Success and invention often come after a series of mistakes and false assumptions. The only time a mistake is a problem is when it is your last attempt. Do not give up!

Use the checklist below to help you develop your problem-solving skills! You may want to print multiple copies of this page to use throughout the course while solving problems.

In this guide, you have explored a number of problem-solving strategies, received a variety of tips for success, and reviewed the five-step Plan for Solving a Word Problem.

Below is a helpful checklist to bring all the information together that you've learned to help you develop into a great problem solver. As you use the checklist to remind yourself of how to approach problems, your problem-solving skills will improve not only in this course but also in all aspects of study.

Prior to solving the problem:

☐ Read the problem more than once.

☐ Be sure you understand what the problem says.

☐ Restate the problem in your own words.

☐ Try to remember a similar problem you have worked.

☐ Identify the information that directly applies to solving this problem.

☐ Disregard information you don't need.

As you solve the problem:

☐ Think about the steps required to solve the problem.

☐ Check your work as you go.

☐ Stop and rethink your steps.

Try different strategies:

☐ Experiment and simulate.

☐ Simplify and reduce the problem.

☐ Recognize a pattern in the problem.

☐ Guess and check.

☐ Use logical deduction.

☐ Work the problem backward.

☐ Draw a picture.

☐ Apply your own unique strategies.

After solving the problem:

☐ Check to see that your calculations are correct.

☐ Ask yourself whether your answer is reasonable.

☐ Solve the problem another way and compare the solutions.

Most of all, enjoy the experience.

Student Guide

Core Focus: Equations with Rational Numbers

Rational numbers include integers, fractions, and decimals. You've seen numerous equations involving integers, but equations can contain all forms of rational numbers. In this lesson, you will learn how to solve equations that involve fractions and decimals.

Goals for This Lesson
- Solve equations involving rational coefficients.

Graded Activities in This Lesson
There is no graded activity associated with this lesson.

Materials
Intermediate Mathematics C: A Reference Guide and Problem Sets, pages 74–75

Keywords
none

Learn: Solving Equations Involving Rational Numbers [online]
Use the space below to take notes during this activity.

Overview

Solving Equations

Summary

Offline Learning: Core Focus: Equations with Rational Numbers [offline]
Read pages 74–75.

Problem Sets
Complete Problems 1–9 odd on page 75.

Student Guide

Equations Review

In this unit, you learned to solve equations that involve addition, subtraction, multiplication, and division, and you learned to solve equations with variables on one or both sides of the equals sign. Now it's time to pull together what you have learned.

Goals for This Lesson

- Solve addition or subtraction equations.
- Solve addition or subtraction equations involving simplification.
- Solve a word problem involving addition or subtraction.
- Write an equation that models a word problem involving addition or subtraction.
- Solve an equation involving division.
- Solve an equation involving multiplication.
- Write an equation that models a word problem involving multiplication or division.
- Solve a word problem that involves an equation with multiplication or division.
- Solve an equation involving more than one transformation.
- Write an equation to solve a word problem that involves an equation with multiple transformations.
- Solve an equation that has a variable on both sides.
- Solve word problems that involve equations with variables on both sides.
- Identify an equation as an identity, a contradiction, or neither.
- Determine whether given linear equations have one solution, no solutions, or infinite solutions.
- Create equations that have one solution, no solution, or infinite solutions.
- Solve equations involving rational coefficients.

Graded Activities in This Lesson

There is no graded activity associated with this lesson.

Materials

Intermediate Mathematics C: A Reference Guide and Problem Sets, pages 76–77

Optional
calculator

Keywords

contradiction: an equation that is true for no values of the variable

empty set: the set with no elements, also known as the null set

equivalent equations: equations that have the same solution

inverse operations: mathematical operations that undo each other, such as addition and subtraction or multiplication and division

solution set of an equation: the set of all solutions of an equation

transformation: an operation performed on an equation or an inequality that produces a simpler equivalent statement

transform an equation: to rewrite an equation or inequality as an equivalent equation or inequality

transformation by addition: adding the same real number to each side of a given equation or inequality

transformation by division: dividing each side of a given equation by the same nonzero real number

transformation by multiplication: multiplying each side of a given equation by the same nonzero real number

transformation by substitution: replacing any expression in a given equation or inequality with an equivalent expression

transformation by subtraction: subtracting the same real number from each side of a given equation

Unit Review: Practice Quiz [online]

The last screen of the practice quiz will show you how many times you attempted each problem. For each problem, record your number of attempts below. Complete the activities and reference guide problems that correspond with the practice quiz problems that took you more than one attempt. Check off the review activities and review problems as you complete them.

Problem 1
Attempts: _____
□ Complete review activities online
□ Complete problems 1–5 on page 50

Problem 2
Attempts: _____
□ Complete review activities online
□ Complete problems 1–4 on page 56

Problem 3
Attempts: _____
□ Complete review activities online
□ Complete problems 1–4 on page 56

Problem 4
Attempts: _____
□ Complete review activities online
□ Complete problems 19–23 on page 57

Problem 5
Attempts: _____
□ Complete review activities online
□ Complete problems 14–18 on page 62

Problem 6
Attempts: _____
□ Complete review activities online
□ Complete problems 14–18 on page 62

Problem 7
Attempts: _____
□ Complete review activities online
□ Complete problems 1–4 on page 65

Problem 8
Attempts: _____
□ Complete review activities online
□ Complete problems 4–16 even on pages 69–70

Problem 9
Attempts: _____
□ Complete review activities online
□ Complete problems 4–16 even on page 69–70

Problem 10
Attempts: _____
□ Complete review activities online
□ Complete problems 5–8 on page 75

Offline Learning: Equations Review [offline]

Complete all the chapter review problems on pages 76–77. Use the topic lookup at the bottom of page 77 to review topics for any problems that were difficult for you.

Student Guide

Unit Test

You have learned to solve linear equations. Now it's time to take the Unit Test.

This Unit Test has two parts—one part that will be scored by the computer and one part that your Learning Coach will score. You will complete the computer-scored part first.

Goals for This Lesson

- Solve addition or subtraction equations.

- Write an equation that models a word problem involving addition or subtraction.

- Solve an equation involving multiplication.

- Write an equation that models a word problem involving multiplication or division.

- Solve an equation involving more than one transformation.

- Solve a word problem that requires writing an equation with multiple transformations.

- Solve an equation that has a variable on both sides.

- Solve word problems that involve equations with variables on both sides.

- Identify an equation as an identity, a contradiction, or neither.

- Determine whether given linear equations have one solution, no solutions, or infinite solutions.

- Create equations that have one solution, no solution, or infinite solutions.

- Solve equations involving rational coefficients.

Graded Activities in This Lesson

Equations Test, Part 1

Equations Test, Part 2

Unit Assessment: Equations Test, Part 1 [online]

You will complete a test covering the main goals of this unit. This part of the test is online. It will be scored by the computer.

Unit Assessment: Equations Test, Part 2 [offline]

This part of the Unit Test is offline.

1. Complete each question on your own. Show all your work.

2. Submit this part to your Learning Coach for a grade.

Student Guide

Extended Problems: Real-World Application

In this lesson, you'll complete the Extended Problems: Real-World Application for the Equations unit.

Goals for This Lesson
- Apply mathematical knowledge and skills to evaluate and analyze real-world situations.

Graded Activities in This Lesson
Extended Problems: Real-World Application

Extended Problems: Real-World Application [offline]
You will complete a graded assignment that focuses on real-world problems in math.

Your Learning Coach will score this assignment.

- **Complete** the assignment on your own.
- **Submit** the completed assignment to your Learning Coach.

Student Guide

Equations in Two Variables

When you are deciding whether to see a movie or go to the park for the afternoon, many variables come into play: the weather, how much money you have to spend, transportation, and how many people are involved. In this lesson, you will work with variables—just two at a time—as they relate to each other in an equation.

Goals for This Lesson

- Determine whether or not an ordered pair is a solution to a given equation.

- Solve an equation in two variables in terms of one of the variables.

Graded Activities in This Lesson
Lesson Quiz (computer-scored)

Materials
Intermediate Mathematics C: A Reference Guide and Problem Sets, pages 83–87.

Optional
calculator

Keywords
ordered pair of numbers: two numbers, where the first number represents a value on the horizontal axis, and the second number represents a value on the vertical axis, such as (x, y)

solution of an equation with two variables: an ordered pair of numbers that make a sentence true

Groundwork: Preparing for the Lesson [online]

Take this time to review evaluating expressions.

Use the space below to take notes during this activity.

Learn: Equations in Two Variables [online]

You will learn about solutions to equations in two variables and how to solve such equations.

Summarize what you learned in this activity.

1. What kind of solution does an equation in two variables have?

2. How many solutions does an equation in two variables have?

3. If the graph of an equation is a straight line, what do we call the equation?

4. If the graph of an equation is a straight line, where will you find solutions to the equation in the graph?

Worked Examples: Try Equations in Two Variables [online]
Use the space below to work through the examples you see in the online screens.

MathCast: Finding Solutions [online]
View the video to see how to solve a typical problem.

Summary: Equations in Two Variables [online]

Solving equations given ordered pairs is a matter of substituting possible values into the equation.

The solution to an equation with two variables is one or more ordered pairs.

An ordered pair is written in the form (x, y).

To determine whether an ordered pair is a solution to an equation, substitute the values into the equation and test the result.

Offline Learning: Equations in Two Variables [offline]

Read pages 83–85 in the reference guide.

Problem Sets

Complete Problems 1–15 odd, 27, 29 on pages 86–87.

Lesson Assessment: Equations in Two Variables Quiz [online]

Now go back online to complete the Lesson Quiz.

Student Guide

Graphs

The imaginary lines of latitude and longitude form a coordinate grid over the earth. When ship navigators want to describe a ship's location, they use these lines to develop a pair of coordinates or points that correspond to the ship's location on a map. The coordinate plane in algebra is a grid as well, but it is a grid on a flat surface. Countless individuals in business, industry, and science use the graphs of points and lines on a coordinate plane to compare and model real-world data.

Goals for This Lesson
- Graph a point when given an ordered pair.
- Identify a point on a graph, given specific criteria.
- Identify the quadrant for a point on a graph.

Graded Activities in This Lesson
Lesson Quiz (computer-scored)

Materials
Intermediate Mathematics C: A Reference Guide and Problem Sets, pages 88–92.
graph paper
straightedge

Optional
calculator

Keywords
coordinate axes: the *x*- and *y*-axes in a coordinate plane

coordinates of a point: the *x*- and *y*-coordinates of a point, written as an ordered pair of numbers

ordered pair: a pair of numbers in which the first number is the x-coordinate and the second number is the y-coordinate of the location of a point

origin: the zero point on a number line

quadrant: one of the four regions into which the coordinate axes separate the coordinate plane

x-axis: the horizontal number line in a coordinate plane

y-axis: the vertical number line in a coordinate plane

Groundwork: Preparing for the Lesson [online]
Before beginning this lesson, take a moment to review your skills in evaluating expressions.

Use the space below to take notes during this activity.

Learn: The Coordinate Plane and Plotting Points [online]

You will learn the fundamentals of graphing in a coordinate plane.

Summarize what you learned in this activity.

1. Draw a coordinate plane and label the *x*-axis, the *y*-axis, and Quadrants I–IV.

2. What is the origin? Plot and label it in the coordinate plane you just constructed.

3. What are ordered pairs?

Worked Examples: Try the Coordinate Plane and Plotting Points

[online]
Use the space below to work through the examples you see in the online screens

Summary: Graphs [online]

You can graph points and lines in a plane and interpret information from the graphs.

An ordered pair designates the location of a point in a plane.

Offline Learning: Graphs [offline]

Read pages 88–89 in the reference guide.

Problem Sets
Complete Problems 1–25 and 27–28 on pages 90–92.

Extra Practice (optional)
Complete Problems 26, 29, 30 on pages 91–92.

Lesson Assessment: Graphs Quiz [online]

Now go back online to complete the Lesson Quiz.

Student Guide

Lines and Intercepts

This lesson focuses on various ways to write equations and graph them. Have you ever wondered how equations can be used in real life? With phones being more accessible to people now, consumers need to be more aware of what the best deals are. One long-distance company charges a $5 flat fee for phone service per month plus 10 cents per minute. The equation that can describe the cost of using the phone is modeled by $C = 0.10x + 5$ where x is the number of calling minutes. Writing and graphing equations is what this lesson is all about.

Goals for the Lesson
- Use a graph to determine if a set of points is collinear.
- Write the equation of a line in standard form.
- Use intercepts to graph a linear equation on a coordinate plane.
- Find the intercepts of a line.

Graded Activities in This Lesson
Lesson Quiz (computer-scored)

Materials
"Lines and Intercepts" in *Algebra I: A Reference Guide and Problem Sets*
graph paper
straightedge

Optional
Lines and Intercepts Solutions

Keywords and Pronunciation
coordinate axes: the *x*- and *y*-axes in a coordinate plane

coordinate plane: a plane marked with one pair of perpendicular number lines used to graph ordered pairs of numbers

coordinates of a point: the *x*- and *y*-coordinates of a point, written as an ordered pair of numbers

collinear: three or more points are collinear if a straight line can be drawn through the given points

graph of an equation with two variables: the line or curve consisting of all points whose coordinates satisfy an equation

graph of an ordered pair: the point in a coordinate plane associated with an ordered pair of real numbers

horizontal axis: also *x-axis*; the horizontal number line in a coordinate plane

linear equation: a polynomial equation of degree 1

origin: the zero point on a number line

plot a point: locate the graph of an ordered pair of real numbers in a coordinate plane

quadrant: one of the four regions into which the coordinate axes separate the coordinate plane

solution of an equation with two variables: an ordered pair of numbers that make a sentence true

standard form of a linear equation: $Ax + By = C$, where A, B, and C are integers and A and B are not both zero

vertical axis: also *y-axis*; the vertical number line in a coordinate plane

x-axis: the horizontal number line in a coordinate plane

x-intercept: the point at which the graph crosses the *x*-axis

y-axis: the vertical number line in a coordinate plane

y-intercept: the point at which the graph crosses the *y*-axis

Groundwork: Preparing for the Lesson [online]
Evaluating expressions

Learn: Collinear Points [online]
A set of points is collinear if you can draw a single line through all the points.
Notes

Worked Examples: Lines and Intercepts [online]

Use this space to work out the online examples before checking the answers.

Notes

MathCast: Finding and Using Intercepts [online]

View the video to see how to solve a typical problem.

Summary: Lines and Intercepts [online]

- To determine whether three given points are collinear or noncollinear

    1. Plot the given set of points on a piece of graph paper.

    2. If possible, draw a line through all three points.

    If you can draw a single line through all three points, the points are *collinear*. If you cannot draw a single line through all three points, the points are *noncollinear*.

- A linear equation is in standard form if it is in the form $Ax + By = C$, where A, B, and C are integers.

- When graphing linear equations by plotting intercepts, remember that the x-intercept is the point where the graph crosses the x-axis, and the y-intercept is where the graph crosses the y-axis.

    1. Find the x-intercept by substituting 0 for y and solving the equation for x.

    2. Find the y-intercept by substituting 0 for x and solving the equation for y.

    3. Plot the two intercepts and draw a line connecting the points.

Skills Update: Practice Your Math Skills [online]

Complete the Skills Update online.

Offline Learning: Lines and Intercepts [offline]

In the Book

Read pages 197–199 through Example 3 in the Reference Guide.

Lesson Main Points

- You can verify that three given points are collinear by plotting the points on graph paper and drawing a straight line through all three points.

- You can write a linear equation in standard form by writing it in the form $Ax + By = C$, where A, B, and C are integers.

- You can find the x-intercept by substituting 0 for y and solving the equation for x.

- You can find the y-intercept by substituting 0 for x and solving the equation for y.

Do the Math

- Being able to graph linear equations is key to your future success in algebra. You should know how to tell whether an equation is a linear equation and whether the linear equation is in standard form.

- If an equation is a linear equation, but it is not in standard form, you can transform it using the properties of algebra to convert it to standard form. For example, look at these equations:

Not in Standard Form	Standard Form
$\frac{1}{2}x + 4y = 12$	$x + 8y = 24$
$y = 3x - 2$	$-3x + y = -2$
$x + y - 1 = x - y + 1$	$y = 2$

Remember: *There are many ways to change equations to make new equations with exactly the same solutions. Doing so can make the solutions much easier to see, or (as in a graph) it can show other features of the relationship the equation describes.*

Remember: *The graph of an equation is a visual representation of all the values of the variables that make the equation a true statement. The graph of a linear equation is actually an infinite set of points that you draw as a line.*

Consider this example of a linear equation that is definitely not in standard form.

Graph this equation:

$$\frac{x}{8} - \frac{y}{2} = \frac{1}{4}$$

Rewrite the equation in standard form.

$\dfrac{x}{8} - \dfrac{y}{2} = \dfrac{1}{4}$ Original equation

$x - 4y = 2$ Multiply by the least common denominator, 8.

Find the line's intercepts.

$(0) - 4y = 2$

$y = -\dfrac{2}{4} = -\dfrac{1}{2}$ Substitute 0 for x, and solve for y.

$x - 4(0) = 2$

$x = 2$ Substitute 0 for y, and solve for x.

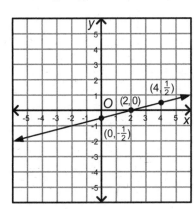

Graph the equation using the points you have identified above: $\left(0, -\dfrac{1}{2}\right)$ and $(2, 0)$.

Use a third point to verify your graph.   It appears that the line's graph passes through the point $\left(4, \dfrac{1}{2}\right)$, so check that it is a solution to the equation.

$\dfrac{4}{8} - \dfrac{y}{2} = \dfrac{1}{4}$

$4 - 4y = 2$

$ -4y = -2$

$y = \dfrac{-2}{-4} = \dfrac{1}{2}$

Verify that the point $\left(4, \dfrac{1}{2}\right)$ is on the graph of the line. Substitute 4 for x and solve for y to see if you get $\dfrac{1}{2}$.

Problem Sets

Complete Problems 1–7 odd, 10–12, and 15–23 odd on page 201.

Key It In (optional)

Graphing lines on a graphing calculator is a simple operation. If you do not have your own graphing calculator and have not yet downloaded GraphCalc, you can find the link to the download page in Resources. Below is the procedure you would use in GraphCalc to graph lines in $y =$ form.

For this exercise, use the equations you converted to standard form in the Do the Math section of the Student Guide. You will convert the equations to the $y =$ form.

First, you'll need to rewrite the calculation in $y =$ form.

Standard Form	$y =$ Form
$x + 8y = 24$	$y = \dfrac{-x}{8} + 3$
$-3x + y = -2$	$y = 3x - 2$

Now, you're ready to graph the equations. Be sure to check that the x and y scale values are set for a maximum of 10 and a minimum of –10. Select the **2D Graph, Range & Precision** menu item, then select the **Range & Precision** tab to check or adjust these values.

You should also clear any lines currently displaying on the screen. To do this, select the **Clear** menu item from the **Edit** menu.

GraphCalc Operation	Keystrokes
Access the basic graphing functions.	Select the **Graph 1** tab.
Enter the equation $y = \dfrac{-x}{8} + 3$.	Click the **y1** check box on the Equations tab; TYPE **–x / 8 + 3** OK

Once you have entered the equation and set the appropriate range, you can see the graph. Try entering the other equations in other $y =$ input boxes. The graph of each equation will display in a different color. If you try other equations, you might find you need to change your range to see them well.

Lesson Assessment: Lines and Intercepts Quiz [online]

Now go back online to complete the lesson quiz.

Student Guide

Slope

How important is the slope of a line? Consider, for example, the significance of the slope of a road for the driver of a tractor trailer. Imagine the driver attempting to make it to the top of the road. Now think of the stress on the tractor's brakes when, fully loaded, the tractor makes its way back down the road.

In this lesson, you will look closely at lines and slopes.

Goals for This Lesson
- Determine whether a line has positive slope, negative slope, zero slope, or undefined slope.
- Find the slope of a line given two points.
- Find the slope of a line given the equation of the line.

Graded Activities in This Lesson
Lesson Quiz (computer-scored)

Materials
Intermediate Mathematics C: A Reference Guide and Problem Sets, pages 98–103
graph paper
straightedge

Optional
calculator

Keywords
slope: a number that describes the steepness of a line, computed as the ratio of the change in the *y*-coordinates to the change in the *x*-coordinates (the ratio of rise to run) when moving from one point on the line to another point on the line

Groundwork: Preparing for the Lesson [online]
You will review how to subtract negative numbers.

Learn: How Steep Is That Slope? [online]
You will study rise and run a little more closely.

Directions for using the Graphing Tool:

1. Use the sliders to enter the following pair of points: (–3, –2) and (5, 4).

2. Look at the line. Does it show a positive slope or a negative slope?

3. Predict the value of the slope using the rise and run displayed in the graph.

4. Type in the values for y_2, y_1, x_2, and x_1 in the labeled fields of the formula in the lower right of the screen.

5. Enter the difference of $y_2 – y_1$ and the difference of $x_2 – x_1$.

6. Enter the value for *m*.

7. Click Check.

8. If your answer is correct, repeat this process with two more sets of points of your choice.

9. If your answer is incorrect, try again or click Show Me.

Summarize what you learned in this activity.

1. What is the slope of a line?

2. What is the formula for finding the slope of a line?

3. If you know the standard form of the equation of a line, how can you find the slope of the line?

4. What are the rise and run of a line?

5. Complete the following sentences:

If you travel from left to right to get from one point to another on a line in a coordinate plane, then the

_____ (rise, run) is _____. (positive, negative)

If you travel from right to left to get from one point to another on a line in a coordinate plane, then the

_____ (rise, run) is _____. (positive, negative)

If you move upward to get from one point to another on a line in a coordinate plane, then the

_____ (rise, run) is _____. (positive, negative)

If you move downward to get from one point to another on a line in a coordinate plane, then the

_____ (rise, run) is _____. (positive, negative)

Worked Examples: Try Slope [online]

Directions for using the Graphing Learning Tool:

1. Type in the coordinates (1, −1) for (x_1, y_1), and (−5, 2) for (x_2, y_2). Hit Enter after each entry.

2. Enter the values for y_2, y_1, x_2, and x_1 in the labeled fields of the formula in the lower right of the screen.

3. Enter the difference of $y_2 − y_1$ and the difference of $x_2 − x_1$.

4. Enter the value for m. This is the slope of the line.

5. Select Check.

6. If your response is correct, repeat the process for the next set of points:

$(2, -1) \rightarrow (x_1, y_1)$

$(5, -2) \rightarrow (x_2, y_2)$

7. If your response is not correct, try again or select Show Me.

Use the space below to work through the examples you see in the online screens.

MathCast: Slope [online]

View the video to see how to solve a typical problem.

Summary: Slope [online]

Slope is a measure of the steepness of a line. For any given line, the slope is always the same. It doesn't matter which pair of points you use to calculate the slope.

To calculate the slope, given the equation of a line, start by finding two ordered pairs on the line. Once you have two points, you can start from either one, but starting with the point to the left and moving to the right can help you remain consistent.

When finding coordinates on a line where you are given the equation, you can use any two points. However, two of the easiest are found by first letting x equal 0 and then calculating y, and then letting y equal 0 and then calculating x.

Offline Learning: Slope [offline]

Read pages 98–101 in the reference guide.

Problem Sets

Complete Problems 1–27 odd on pages 102–103.

Extra Practice (optional)

Complete Problems 2–28 even on pages 102–103 for extra practice.

Lesson Assessment: Slope Quiz [online]

Now go back online to complete the Lesson Quiz.

Student Guide

Simple Linear Graphs

The origin of the coordinate plane is the point where the *x*- and *y*-axes intersect. You use the origin, or point (0, 0), to describe the location of other points on the graph. For instance, the point (3, −4) is 3 units to the right of the origin and 4 units down.

Suppose you drew a line that passes through (0, 0) and (3, −4). That line would pass through the origin. In this lesson, you will learn how to write an equation of a line that passes through the origin.

Goals for This Lesson
- Derive the equation $y = mx$ for a line that passes through the origin.
- Identify coordinates on a line given an equation in the form $y = mx$.
- Graph equations of the form $y = mx$ by plotting points.
- Graph equations of the form $y = mx$ using the origin and the slope.

Graded Activities in This Lesson
Lesson Quiz (computer-scored)

Materials
Intermediate Mathematics C: A Reference Guide and Problem Sets, pages 104–108

Optional
calculator

Keywords
origin: the intersection of the axes on a coordinate plane; the point (0, 0)

slope: a number that describes the steepness of a line, computed as the ratio of the change in the *y*-coordinates to the change in the *x*-coordinates when moving from one point on a line to another point on the same line

Groundwork: Preparing for the Lesson [online]
You will find the slope of a line using either two points or the equation of the line.

Learn: Equation of a Line Through the Origin [online]
You will discover the form of an equation of a line that passes through the origin by using the slope formula.

Summarize what you learned in this activity.

How can you write the equation of a line that passes through the origin with slope *m*?

Learn: Graphing a Line Through the Origin [online]

You will graph lines that pass through the origin by plotting points and by using the origin and the slope of the line.

Summarize what you learned in this activity.
1. How can you graph a line through the origin by using two points on the line?

2. How can you graph a line through the origin by using the origin and the slope?

Worked Examples: Graphing a Line Through the Origin [online]

Use the space below to work through the examples you see in the online screens.

Learn: Writing an Equation from a Graph [online]

You will write the equation of a line by looking at its graph.

Summarize what you learned in this activity.
1. How can you write the equation of a line from its graph, using rise over run?

2. How can you write the equation of a line from its graph, using the slope formula?

Worked Examples: Writing an Equation from a Graph [online]

Use the space below to work through the examples you see in the online screens.

Summary: Simple Linear Graphs [online]

Here are some important things to remember about lines that pass through the origin:

- The equation of a line that passes through the origin is written $y = mx$, where m is the slope of the line.
- One way to graph a line through the origin is to substitute x-values into the equation $y = mx$ and determine two ordered pairs that lie on the line.
- Another way to graph a line through the origin is to plot the origin and then use the slope, m, to determine another point on the line.
- To write the equation of a line that passes through the origin from its graph, determine the slope of the line and substitute the slope for m in the equation $y = mx$.

Offline Learning: Practice: Simple Linear Graphs [offline]

Read pages 104–106 in the reference guide.

Problem Sets

Complete Problems 7–9, 13–16, and 23–25 on pages 107–108.

Lesson Assessment: Simple Linear Graphs Quiz [online]

Go back online to complete the Lesson Quiz.

Student Guide

Using Slope as a Rate

When driving to the store, you pass a speed limit sign. The maximum speed is 45 mph. At the store, you see that oranges are one sale: $2 for 3 oranges. There is a long line at the register. Every 15 min, only 4 people are checked out.

Three rates are described in the paragraph above.

Goals for This Lesson
- Use a rate to model and solve problems.
- Interpret a slope as a rate for a given problem context.

Graded Activities in This Lesson
Lesson Quiz (computer-scored)

Materials
Intermediate Mathematics C: A Reference Guide and Problem Sets, pages 109–114

Optional
calculator

Keywords
rate: a ratio that compares quantities of different kinds of units

slope: a number that describes the steepness of a line, computed as the ratio of the change in the *y*-coordinates to the change in the *x*-coordinates when moving from one point on a line to another point on the same line

unit rate: a rate that has a denominator of 1

Groundwork: Ratio, Rate, and Unit Rate [online]
You will review ratios and rates.

Learn: Rate Problems [online]
You will learn how to find unit rates, how to graph a line given data values or a rate, and how to interpret the slope of a line as a rate.

Summarize what you learned in this activity.
1. What is a unit rate?

2. What information is needed to interpret a slope as a unit rate?

3. Summarize the steps used to graph a line that represents a specific situation.

Worked Examples: Rate Problems [online]
Use the space below to work through the examples you see in the online screens.

Summary: Using Slope as a Rate [online]
When a line represents a real-world situation, the slope can be interpreted as a rate.

For every increase of *x* units, there is a change of *y* units. If *y* is positive, the change is an increase. If *y* is negative, the change is a decrease.

To interpret the slope as a unit rate, the rate must be given in terms of one of the *x* units.

Offline Learning: Practice: Using Slope as a Rate [offline]
Read pages 109–112 in the reference guide.

Problem Sets
Complete Problems 1–11 odd, 12–13, and 15–19 odd on pages 113–114.

Extra Practice (optional)
Complete Problems 2–10 even, 14, and 16–20 even on pages 113–114.

Lesson Assessment: Using Slope as a Rate Quiz [online]
Go back online to complete the Lesson Quiz.

Student Guide

Slope and Similar Triangles

You've learned about the slope of a line. Have you ever wondered whether the slope of a line changes as you move along the line? In this lesson, you will learn how to show that the slope of a line doesn't change and that it's constant. You'll do this by using similar triangles.

Goals for This Lesson
- Use similar triangles to analyze the slope of a line.

Graded Activities in This Lesson
Lesson Quiz (computer-scored)

Materials
Intermediate Mathematics C: A Reference Guide and Problem Sets, pages 115–117

Optional
calculator

Keywords
similar figures: figures that have the same shape but not necessarily the same size

Groundwork: Similar Triangles [online]
You will determine whether two right triangles are similar.

Use the spaces below to take notes during this activity.

Learn: Similar Right Triangles and Slope [online]
You will learn how to use similar right triangles to show that the slope of a line is constant.

Summarize what you learned in this activity.
1. What is true about all of the right triangles whose hypotenuses lie along the same line?

2. What is true about the slopes of the hypotenuses of all of the right triangles that lie along the same line?

Worked Examples: Similar Right Triangles and Slope [online]

Use the space below to work through the examples you see in the online screens.

Summary: Slope and Similar Triangles [online]

Any two points on a line create a hypotenuse of a right triangle. Right triangles whose hypotenuses lie along a line are similar. The slopes of the hypotenuses of similar right triangles are always equal. Since there are an infinite number of points along a line, there are an infinite number of right triangles whose hypotenuses lie along a line. The slope of the line is equal to the slope of the hypotenuses. Therefore, the slope of a line is constant.

Offline Learning: Slope and Similar Triangles [offline]

Read pages 115–116 in the reference guide.

Problem Sets

Complete Problems 1–8 on page 117.

Lesson Assessment: Slope and Similar Triangles Quiz [online]

Go back online to complete the Lesson Quiz.

Student Guide

Comparing Proportional Relationships

Suppose you're a furniture store manager and you're comparing the profit per couch sold for two store locations. Store A's profits and couches sold are displayed in a graph. Store B's profits and couches sold are displayed in a table. How could you determine which store is earning more money per couch? When you make comparisons like this one, you're comparing two proportional relationships. In this lesson, you will learn how to compare proportional relationships that are displayed in different ways, such as tables, graphs, or equations.

Goals for This Lesson
- Compare two proportional relationships that are represented in different ways.

Graded Activities in This Lesson
Lesson Quiz (computer-scored)

Materials
Intermediate Mathematics C: A Reference Guide and Problem Sets, pages 118–123

Optional
calculator

Keywords
proportional relationship: a relationship that can be described by an equation of the form $y = kx$, where k is the constant of proportionality

Groundwork: Proportional Relationships [online]
You will identify equations as being proportional or not proportional.

Use the spaces below to take notes during this activity.

Learn: Tables, Graphs, and Equations [online]

You will compare the rates of proportional relationships that are expressed as tables, graphs, or equations.

Summarize what you learned in this activity.

When you compare two proportional relationships, how do you compare their rates?

Worked Examples: Tables, Graphs, and Equations [online]

Use the space below to work through the examples you see in the online screens.

Summary: Comparing Proportional Relationships [online]

Regardless of how two proportional relationships are expressed, you must always compare their slopes in order to compare the relationships. The relationship with the greater slope has the greater rate.

Offline Learning: Comparing Proportional Relationships [offline]

Read pages 118–120 in the reference guide.

Problem Sets

Complete Problems 1–10 on pages 121–123.

Lesson Assessment: Comparing Proportional Relationships Quiz [online]

Go back online to complete the Lesson Quiz.

Student Guide

Core Focus: Graphs of Proportional Relationships

Your car can travel 20 mi per gallon of gas. You earn $15/h. You can type 34 words per minute. What do all of these have in common? They are all proportional relationships. In this lesson, you will learn how to graph proportional relationships. You will also learn how to interpret the slope of the graph of a proportional relationship as a unit rate.

Goals for This Lesson
- Graph proportional relationships.

- Interpret the unit rate of a proportional relationship as the slope of a graph.

Graded Activities in This Lesson
There is no graded activity associated with this lesson.

Materials
Intermediate Mathematics C: A Reference Guide and Problem Sets, pages 124–125

Optional
calculator

Keywords
none

Learn: Graphing Proportional Relationships [online]
Use the space below to take notes during this activity.

Overview

Drawing Graphs and Interpreting Slopes

Summary

Offline Learning: Core Focus: Graphs of Proportional Relationships [offline]

Read pages 124–125.

Problem Sets

Complete Problems 1–2 on page 125.

Student Guide

Slope and Proportional Thinking Review

In this unit, you learned about working with equations in two variables, graphing points and lines, finding the intercepts of lines, determining and interpreting the slopes of lines, and comparing and graphing proportional relationships. Now it's time to pull together what you have learned.

Goals for This Lesson

- Solve an equation in two variables in terms of one of the variables.

- Determine whether or not an ordered pair is a solution to a given equation.

- Identify a point on a graph, given specific criteria.

- Graph a point when given an ordered pair.

- Identify the quadrant for a point on a graph.

- Write the equation of a line in standard form.

- Use a graph to determine if a set of points is collinear.

- Use intercepts to graph a linear equation on a coordinate plane.

- Determine whether a line has positive slope, negative slope, zero slope, or undefined slope.

- Find the slope of a line given two points.

- Find the slope of a line given the equation of the line.

- Derive the equation $y = mx$ for a line that passes through the origin.

- Identify coordinates on a line given an equation in the form $y = mx$.

- Graph equations of the form $y = mx$ by plotting points.

- Graph equations of the form $y = mx$ using the origin and the slope.

- Interpret a slope as a rate for a given problem context.

- Use a rate to model and solve problems.

- Use similar triangles to analyze the slope of a line.

- Compare two proportional relationships that are represented in different ways.

- Graph proportional relationships.

- Interpret the unit rate of a proportional relationship as the slope of a graph.

Graded Activities in This Lesson
There is no graded activity associated with this lesson.

Materials
Intermediate Mathematics C: A Reference Guide and Problem Sets, pages 126–127

Keywords
collinear: three or more points are collinear if a straight line can be drawn through the given points

coordinate axes: the *x*- and *y*-axes in a coordinate plane

coordinates of a point: the x- and y-coordinates of a point, written as an ordered pair of numbers

graph of an ordered pair: the point in a coordinate plane associated with an ordered pair of real numbers

ordered pair of numbers: two numbers, where the first number represents a value on the horizontal axis, and the second number represents a value on the vertical axis, such as (x, y)

origin: the intersection of the axes on a coordinate plane; the point $(0, 0)$

plot a point: locate the graph of an ordered pair of real numbers in a coordinate plane

proportional relationship: a relationship that can be described by an equation of the form $y = kx$, where k is the constant of proportionality

quadrant: one of the four regions into which the coordinate axes separate the coordinate plane

rate: a ratio that compares quantities of different kinds of units

slope: a number that describes the steepness of a line, computed as the ratio of the change in the y-coordinates to the change in the x-coordinates when moving from one point on a line to another point on the same line

solution of an equation with two variables: an ordered pair of numbers that make a sentence true

standard form of a linear equation: $Ax + By = C$, where A, B, and C are integers and A and B are not both zero

unit rate: a rate that has a denominator of 1

x-axis: the horizontal number line in a coordinate plane

x-intercept: the x-coordinate of a point where a graph intersects the x-axis

y-axis: the vertical number line in a coordinate plane

y-intercept: the y-coordinate of a point where a graph intersects the y-axis

Unit Review: Practice Quiz [online]

The last screen of the Practice Quiz will show you how many times you attempted each problem. For each problem, record your number of attempts below. Complete the activities and reference guide problems that correspond with the Practice Quiz problems that took you more than one attempt. Check off the review activities and review problems as you complete them.

Problem 1
Attempts: _____
□ Complete review activities online
□ Complete Problems 11–21 on page 86

Problem 2
Attempts: _____
□ Complete review activities online
□ Complete Problems 9–16 on pages 90–91

Problem 3
Attempts: _____
□ Complete review activities online
□ Complete Problems 1–5 on page 96

Problem 4
Attempts: _____
□ Complete review activities online
□ Complete Problems 20–24 on page 97

Problem 5
Attempts: _____
□ Complete review activities online
□ Complete Problems 10–15 on pages 102–103

Problem 6
Attempts: _____
□ Complete review activities online
□ Complete Problems 4–9 on page 102

Problem 7
Attempts: _____
□ Complete review activities online
□ Complete Problems 16–20 on page 107

Problem 8
Attempts: _____
□ Complete review activities online
□ Complete Problems 21–24 on pages 107–108

Problem 9
Attempts: _____
□ Complete review activities online
□ Complete Problems 2–5 on page 113

Problem 10
Attempts: _____
□ Complete review activities online
□ Complete Problems 3–6 on pages 121–122

Offline Learning: Slope and Proportional Thinking Review [offline]

Complete all the Chapter Review problems on pages 126–127. Use the Topic Lookup at the bottom of page127 to review topics for any problems that were difficult for you.

Student Guide

Unit Test

You have learned about working with equations in two variables, graphing points and lines, finding the intercepts of lines, determining and interpreting the slopes of lines, and comparing and graphing proportional relationships. Now it's time to take the Unit Test.

This Unit Test has two parts—one part that will be scored by the computer and one part that your Learning Coach will score. You will complete the computer-scored part first.

Goals for This Lesson

- Solve an equation in two variables in terms of one of the variables.

- Determine whether or not an ordered pair is a solution to a given equation.

- Identify a point on a graph, given specific criteria.

- Graph a point when given an ordered pair.

- Identify the quadrant for a point on a graph.

- Write the equation of a line in standard form.

- Use intercepts to graph a linear equation on a coordinate plane.

- Determine whether a line has positive slope, negative slope, zero slope, or undefined slope.

- Find the slope of a line given two points.

- Find the slope of a line given the equation of the line.

- Derive the equation $y = mx$ for a line that passes through the origin.

- Identify coordinates on a line given an equation in the form $y = mx$.

- Graph equations of the form $y = mx$ by plotting points.

- Graph equations of the form $y = mx$ using the origin and the slope.

- Interpret a slope as a rate for a given problem context.

- Use a rate to model and solve problems.

- Compare two proportional relationships that are represented in different ways.

Graded Activities in This Lesson

Slope and Proportional Thinking Unit Test, Part 1

Slope and Proportional Thinking Unit Test, Part 2

Unit Assessment: Slope and Proportional Thinking Test, Part 1 [online]

This part of the Unit Test is online. It will be scored by the computer.

Unit Assessment: Slope and Proportional Thinking Test, Part 2 [offline]

This part of the Unit Test is offline.

1. Complete each question on your own. Show all your work.

2. Submit this part to your Learning Coach for a grade.

Student Guide

Extended Problems: Reasoning

In this lesson, you'll complete Extended Problems: Reasoning for the Slope and Proportional Thinking unit.

Goals for This Lesson
- Analyze complex problems using mathematical knowledge and skills.

Graded Activities in This Lesson
Extended Problems: Reasoning

Extended Problems: Reasoning [offline]
You will complete a graded assignment that focuses on reasoning in math.

Your Learning Coach will score this assignment.

- **Complete** the assignment on your own.
- **Submit** the completed assignment to your Learning Coach.

Student Guide

Slope-Intercept Form

When you are deciding whether to see a movie or go to the park for the afternoon, many variables come into play: the weather, how much money you have to spend, transportation, and how many people are involved. In this lesson, you will work with variables—just two at a time—as they relate to each other in an equation.

Goals for This Lesson
- Find the slope and y-intercept of a line when given its equation in slope-intercept form.
- Transform an equation into slope-intercept form.
- Graph a line when its equation is given as or transformed into slope-intercept form.

Graded Activities in This Lesson
Lesson Quiz (computer-scored)

Materials
Intermediate Mathematics C: A Reference Guide and Problem Sets, pages 133–136.

Optional
calculator

Keywords
slope-intercept form of an equation of a line: the equation of a line in the form $y = mx + b$, where m is the slope and b is the y-intercept

***y*-intercept:** the y-coordinate of a point where a graph intercepts the y-axis

Skills Update: Practice Your Math Skills

Practice using rates to calculate values in a real-world problem.

Groundwork: Preparing for the Lesson [online]
Take this time to review evaluating expressions.

Use the space below to take notes during this activity.

Learn: Slope-Intercept Form [online]

You will learn how to graph a line from an equation in slope-intercept form.

Summarize what you learned in this activity.

1. What is slope-intercept form of a linear equation?

2. How can you tell whether an equation is in slope-intercept form?

3. When an equation is in slope-intercept form, what information does the equation give you about the line?

4. If an equation is not in slope-intercept form, what must you do to get it in slope-intercept form?

Worked Examples: Try Working with Slope-Intercept Form [online]

Use the space below to work through the examples you see in the online screens.

Directions for using the Graphing Learning Tool:

1. Enter the equation $y = 3x + 2$ by typing at the bottom of the screen.

2. Set the sliders for the first point to plot the y-intercept.

3. Starting at the point you just plotted, use the slope to find one more point on the line. Use the sliders for the second point to plot the point you identify.

4. Click Check.

5. If your line is correct, repeat steps 1-4 for the equation $y = \frac{2}{3}x + 6$. If your line is incorrect, try again, or click Show Me.

MathCast: Using Slope-Intercept Form to Graph a Line [online]

View the video to see how to solve a typical problem.

Summary: Slope-Intercept Form [online]

The slope-intercept form of a linear equation is $y = mx + b$, where m is the slope of the line and b is the y-intercept. The slope-intercept form of an equation of a line gives you the slope and the y-intercept, which is all the information you need to graph the line.

An equation is in slope-intercept form if y is alone on one side of the equation. If an equation is not in slope-intercept form, you can use transformations to solve for y to get it in slope-intercept form.

Offline Learning: Slope-Intercept Form [offline]

Read pages 133–135 in the reference guide.

Problem Sets

Complete Problems 1–25 odd on page 136.

Extra Practice (optional)

Complete Problems 2–28 even on page 136.

Lesson Assessment: Slope-Intercept Form Quiz [online]

Now go back online to complete the Lesson Quiz.

Student Guide

The Point-Slope Form

People use tools for various jobs. A saw, a screwdriver, and a wrench are useful, but not for pounding a nail into a wall. In the same way, the slope-intercept form of a linear equation is useful at times. However, there are better ways to express a line, especially when only the most basic information is known. In that case, the point-slope form is a more useful tool, just as a hammer is a more useful tool for pounding in nails.

The different forms of equations are useful in performing many mathematical processes, such as solving word problems and estimating the slope of a graph of a line.

Goals for This Lesson
- Write an equation of a line in point-slope form when given specific criteria or a graph.
- Solve a word problem using the point-slope form of an equation.

Graded Activities in This Lesson
Lesson Quiz (computer-scored)

Materials
Intermediate Mathematics C: A Reference Guide and Problem Sets, pages 137–144

Optional
calculator

Keywords
point-slope form: an equation of a line that passes through the points (x, y), has a slope m, and is given by $y - y_1 = m(x - x_1)$

Skills Update: Practice Your Math Skills [online]

Practice to solving equations to prepare for the lesson.

Groundwork: Preparing for the Lesson [online]

Take this time to review writing equations in slope-intercept form.

Use the space below to take notes during this activity.

Learn: The Point-Slope Form [online]

You will learn how to graph a line from an equation in point-slope form.

Summarize what you learned in this activity.

1. What is the point-slope form of a linear equation?

2. How can you tell whether an equation is in point-slope form?

3. When an equation is in point-slope form, what information does the equation give you about the line?

4. If an equation is not in point-slope form, what must you do to get it into point-slope form?

Worked Examples: Try Working with Point-Slope Form [online]

Use the space below to work through the examples you see in the online screens.

MathCast: Writing Equations in Point-Slope Form [online]

View the video to see how to solve a typical problem.

Summary: The Point-Slope Form [online]

Given a point on a line and the slope, you can write the equation of a line in point-slope form

$$y - y_1 = m (x - x_1)$$

where (x_1, y_1) is the given point and m is the slope. You can transform an equation from point-slope form into slope-intercept form.

Offline Learning: The Point-Slope Form [offline]

Read pages 137–140 in the reference guide.

Problem Sets

Complete Problems 1–27 odd on pages 141–143.

Extra Practice (optional)

Complete Problems 2–28 even on pages 141–144.

Lesson Assessment: The Point-Slope Form Quiz [online]

Now go back online to complete the Lesson Quiz.

Student Guide
Equations From Graphs

Crime fighters depend on collecting factual information and then using logic and scientific tools to solve crimes. You will follow a similar procedure when you collect facts about a given line, apply logic and the rules of mathematics to those facts, and transform the information you've collected into an equation of the line.

Goals for This Lesson
* Write an equation of a line in standard form when given specific criteria.
* Write the equation of a horizontal or vertical line.
* Write an equation of a line in slope-intercept form when given specific criteria.
* Write an equation of a line in point-slope form when given specific criteria.

Graded Activities in This Lesson
Lesson Quiz (computer-scored)

Materials
Intermediate Mathematics C: A Reference Guide and Problem Sets, pages 145–150.

Optional
calculator

Keywords

Skills Update: Practice Your Math Skills [online]

Practice using rates to calculate values in a real-world problem.

Groundwork: Preparing for the Lesson [online]
Take this time to review evaluating expressions.

Use the space below to take notes during this activity.

Learn: Determine That Line! [online]

You will learn how to graph a line from an equation in point-slope form.

Summarize what you learned in this activity.

1. What are the three forms of an equation of a line?

2. What is the minimum amount of information you need in order to write the equation of a line?

3. If you are only given two points on a line but not the slope, what should be your first step toward writing the equation of the line?

4. The equation of a horizontal line is $y = b$. What is b?

5. The equation of a vertical line is $x = c$. What is c?

6. What is the y-intercept of $y = mx$?

Worked Examples: Try Writing Equation from Graphs [online]

Use the space below to work through the examples you see in the online screens.

MathCast: Writing an Equation of a Line in Three Forms [online]

View the video to see how to solve a typical problem.

Summary: Equations from Graphs [online]

Given a point on a line and the slope, you can write the equation of a line in point-slope form

$$y - y_1 = m (x - x_1)$$

where (x_1, y_1) is the given point and m is the slope. You can transform an equation from point-slope form into slope-intercept form.

Offline Learning: Equations from Graphs [offline]

Read pages 145–147 in the reference guide.

Problem Sets

Complete Problems 1–23 odd on pages 147–50.

Extra Practice (optional)

Complete Problems 2–24 even on pages 147–150.

Lesson Assessment: Equations from Graphs Quiz [online]

Now go back online to complete the Lesson Quiz.

Student Guide

Core Focus: Sketching Lines

You can use a linear model to represent real-world situations that involve constant rates of change. When you know two points of a linear model or a point and the slope of a linear model, you can draw its graph. In this lesson, you will learn how to graph a line that models a real-world situation given two points on the line or a point on the line and the line's slope. You will also practice sketching lines for situations for which you do not have actual values.

Goals for This Lesson
- Identify information that can be used to graph a line from a word problem describing a linear relationship.

- Sketch a graph that exhibits the qualitative features of a function that has been described verbally.

Graded Activities in This Lesson
Lesson Quiz (computer-scored)

Materials
Intermediate Mathematics C: A Reference Guide and Problem Sets, pages 151–153

Optional
calculator

Keywords
slope: the equation of a line in the form $y = mx + b$, where m is the slope and b is the y-intercept

y-intercept: the y-coordinate of a point where a graph intersects the y-axis

Groundwork: Writing an Equation from a Graph [online]
Take this time to review writing an equation to describe a graph.

Use the space below to take notes during this activity.

Learn: Sketching Lines Described in Words [online]

You will learn how to sketch a line that is described with words and without an equation.

Summarize what you learned in this activity.

1. What information is needed to sketch a line?

    a. Option A:

    b. Option B:

2. What is the first step in sketching the graph?

3. What values might you need to calculate to sketch the line accurately?

Worked Examples: Try Sketching Lines [online]

Use the space below to work through the examples you see in the online screens.

Offline Learning: Core Focus: Sketching Lines [offline]

Read pages 151–152 in the reference guide.

Problem Sets

Complete Problems 1–3 on page 153.

Lesson Assessment: Core Focus: Sketching Lines Quiz [online]

Now go back online to complete the Lesson Quiz.

Student Guide

Applications: Linear Models

When you hear the word *model*, you might think of something that represents or imitates something else. For instance, a model car is a smaller version of the original that it represents. In mathematics, a model is a mathematical representation of relationships that exist in a real-world situation. In this lesson, you will learn to model problems in which a linear relationship exists between the variables involved, and you will learn to identify when a model is linear.

Goals for This Lesson
- Calculate values for a linear equation in two variables.
- Determine if a word problem is modeled by a linear relationship or not.

Graded Activities in This Lesson
Lesson Quiz (computer-scored)

Materials
Intermediate Mathematics C: A Reference Guide and Problem Sets, pages 154–157

Optional
calculator
graph paper

Groundwork: Preparing for the Lesson [online]
To prepare for this lesson, review solving equations in two variables, as well as identifying the slope and *y*-intercept of a line written in slope-intercept form.

Notes

Learn: Using Linear Models [online]

In this activity, you will apply what you've learned about solving equations in two variables, plotting points to graph a line, and using equations in slope-intercept form to model real-world problems. You will also learn how to determine whether a linear relationship exists between the variables in a problem. Use the space below to follow along with the online problems.

Notes

How can you tell whether a model is linear?

Worked Examples: Applications: Linear Models [online]

Use the space below to work through the examples you see in the online screens.

Notes

Summary: Applications: Linear Models [online]

When a problem has a linear model, the graph is a straight line and the equation can be written in slope-intercept form.

Offline Learning: Applications: Linear Models [offline]

Read pages 154–155 in the reference guide.

Problem Sets

Complete Problems 1–27 odd on pages 155–157.

Extra Practice (optional)

Complete Problems 2–26 even on pages 155–157.

Lesson Assessment: Applications: Linear Models Quiz [online]

Now go back online to complete the Lesson Quiz.

Student Guide

Core Focus: Linear Models

You have learned to write and graph linear equations using slope and points on a line. Situations in life can often be modeled using linear equations and their graphs. For instance, the graph of your growth over time would be a line. You could write an equation from the graph that models your growth. In this lesson, you will write equations for real-world situations from word problems, tables, and graphs.

Goals for This Lesson
- Write an equation to represent a linear relationship described in a word problem.

- Determine the rate of change or specified values of a linear relationship described in a real-world context.

Graded Activities in This Lesson
Lesson Quiz (computer-graded)

Materials
Intermediate Mathematics C: A Reference Guide and Problem Sets, pages 158–160

Optional
calculator

Keywords
slope: a number that describes the steepness of a line, computed as the ratio of the change in the *y*-coordinates to the change in the *x*-coordinates when moving from one point on a line to another point on the same line

y-intercept: the point where a graph crosses the *y*-axis

Groundwork: Preparing for the Lesson [online]
You will review writing equations in slope-intercept and point-slope forms.

Summarize what you learned in this activity.
1. What is slope-intercept form?

2. What is point-slope form?

Learn: Linear Equations from Word Problems [offline]
Use the space below to take notes during this activity.

Overview

Writing Linear Equations from a Table

Writing Linear Equations from a Graph

Summary

Worked Examples: Linear Equations from Word Problems
[online]

Use the space below to work through the examples you see in the online screens.

Offline Learning: Core Focus: Linear Models [offline]
Read pages 158–159.

Problem Sets
Complete Problems 1–3 on page 160.

Lesson Assessment: Core Focus: Linear Models Quiz [online]
Go back online to complete the Lesson Quiz.

Student Guide

Core Focus: Interpreting Linear Models

Real-world problems can often be modeled by linear equations. For instance, calculating your earnings at an hourly rate is a linear relationship. If you write an equation that represents how much you earn, you can use that equation to predict how much you will earn in the future or how much you can save over time. In this lesson, you will learn how linear equations can help you solve real-world problems.

Goals for This Lesson
- Interpret the rate of change and initial amount of a linear relationship described in a word problem.

- Describe how the form of a mathematical expression corresponds to an interpretation of a word problem.

- Rewrite an expression using an alternate form to represent a word problem.

Graded Activities in This Lesson
There is no graded activity associated with this lesson.

Materials
Intermediate Mathematics C: A Reference Guide and Problem Sets, pages 161–163

Optional
calculator

Keywords and Pronunciation
slope: a number that describes the steepness of a line, computed as the ratio of the change in the *y*-coordinates to the change in the *x*-coordinates when moving from one point on a line to another point on the same line

y-intercept: the point where a graph crosses the *y*-axis

rate of change: the rate at which quantities change over time in a linear relationship; the rate of change is the slope of the line

initial amount: the beginning value of a linear relationship before any time has passed; the initial amount, also known initial value, is the *y*-intercept of the line

Learn: Interpreting Linear Models [online]
Use the space below to take notes during this activity.

Overview

Interpreting Word Problems with Graphs

Interpreting Word Problems with Tables

Interpreting Word Problems

Summary

Offline Learning: Core Focus: Interpreting Linear Models

[offline]
Read pages 161–162.

Problem Sets
Complete Problems 1–3 on page 163.

Student Guide

Unit Review

In this unit, you have learned how to write equations and graph lines using slope-intercept form, standard form, and point-slope form. You have also learned to solve and interpret word problems that represent linear situations using graphs and tables. Now it's time to pull together what you have learned.

Goals for This Lesson

- Find the slope and *y*-intercept of a line when given its equation in slope-intercept form.

- Find the *y*-intercept of a line when given its equation in slope-intercept form.

- Transform an equation into slope-intercept form.

- Graph a line when its equation is given as or transformed into slope-intercept form.

- Write an equation of a line in point-slope form when given specific criteria or a graph.

- Solve a word problem using the point-slope form of an equation.

- Graph a line in point-slope form.

- Write an equation of a line in point-slope form when given specific criteria.

- Write an equation of a line in standard form when given specific criteria.

- Write an equation of a horizontal or vertical line.

- Write an equation of a line in slope-intercept form when given specific criteria.

- Calculate values for a linear equation in two variables.

- Determine if a word problem is modeled by a linear relationship or not.

- Write an equation in slope-intercept form to model a given word problem.

- Identify information that can be used to graph a line from a word problem describing a linear relationship.

- Sketch a graph that exhibits the qualitative features of a function that has been described verbally.

- Write an equation to represent a linear relationship described in a word problem.

- Interpret the rate of change and initial amount of a linear relationship described in a word problem.

Graded Activities in This Lesson

There is no graded activity associated with this lesson.

Materials

Intermediate Mathematics C: A Reference Guide and Problem Sets, pages 164–165

Optional

calculator

Keywords

initial amount: the beginning value of a linear relationship before any time has passed; the initial amount, also known as initial value, is the *y*-intercept of the line

point-slope form: $y - y_1 = m(x - x_1)$, where (x_1, y_1) is a given point on a line and m is the slope

rate of change: the rate at which quantities change over time in a linear relationship; the rate of change is the slope of the line

slope: a number that describes the steepness of a line, computed as the ratio of the change in the y-coordinates to the change in the x-coordinates when moving from one point on a line to another point on the same line

slope-intercept form of an equation of a line: the equation of a line in the form $y = mx + b$, where m is the slope and b is the y-intercept

x-intercept: the x-coordinate of a point where a graph intersects the x-axis

y-intercept: the y-coordinate of a point where a graph intersects the y-axis

Unit Review: Practice Quiz [online]

The last screen of the Practice Quiz will show you how many times you attempted each problem. For each problem, record your number of attempts below. Complete the activities and reference guide problems that correspond with the Practice Quiz problems that took you more than one attempt. Check off the review activities and review problems as you complete them.

Problem 1
Attempts: _____
□ Complete review activities online
□ Complete problems 6–12 on page 136

Problem 2
Attempts: _____
□ Complete review activities online
□ Complete problems 1–9 on page 141

Problem 3
Attempts: _____
□ Complete review activities online
□ Complete problems 17–24 on page 150

Problem 4
Attempts: _____
□ Complete review activities online
□ Complete problems 10–15 on pages 141–142

Problem 5
Attempts: _____
□ Complete review activities online
□ Complete problems 21–27 on page 157

Problem 6
Attempts: _____
□ Complete review activities online
□ Complete problems 1–3 on page 160

Problem 7
Attempts: _____
□ Complete review activities online
□ Complete problems 1–3 on page 163

Problem 8
Attempts: _____
☐ Complete review activities online
☐ Complete problems 1–10 on pages 155–156

Problem 9
Attempts: _____
☐ Complete review activities online
☐ Complete problems 1–3 on page 160

Problem 10
Attempts: _____
☐ Complete review activities online
☐ Complete problems 1–3 on page 160

Offline Learning: Practice: Lines Review [online]

Complete all the Chapter Review problems on pages 164–165. Use the Topic Lookup at the bottom of page 165 to review topics for any problems that were difficult for you.

Student Guide

Unit Test

You have learned how to write equations and graph lines using slope-intercept form, standard form, and point-slope form. You have also learned to solve and interpret word problems that represent linear situations using graphs and tables. Now it's time to take the Unit Test.

This Unit Test has two parts—one part that will be scored by the computer and one part that your Learning Coach will score. You will complete the computer-scored part first.

Goals for This Lesson

- Find the slope and *y*-intercept of a line when given its equation in slope-intercept form.

  Transform an equation into slope-intercept form.

- Graph a line when its equation is given as or transformed into slope-intercept form.

- Write an equation of a line in point-slope form when given specific criteria or a graph.

- Solve a word problem using the point-slope form of an equation.

- Graph a line in point-slope form.

- Write an equation of a line in point-slope form when given specific criteria or a graph.

- Write an equation of a line in standard form when given specific criteria.

- Write an equation of a horizontal or vertical line.

- Write an equation of a line in slope-intercept form when given specific criteria.

- Calculate values for a linear equation in two variables.

- Write an equation in slope-intercept form to model a given word problem.

- Identify information that can be used to graph a line from a word problem describing a linear relationship.

- Sketch a graph that exhibits the qualitative features of a function that has been described verbally.

- Write an equation to represent a linear relationship described in a word problem.

- Interpret the rate of change and initial amount of a linear relationship described in a word problem.

- Determine the rate of change or specified values of a linear relationship described in a real-world context.

Graded Activities in This Lesson

Lines Unit Test, Part 1

Lines Unit Test, Part 2

Unit Assessment: Lines Test, Part 1 [online]

This part of the Unit Test is online. It will be scored by the computer.

Unit Assessment: Lines Test, Part 2 [offline]

This part of the Unit Test is offline.

1. Complete each question on your own. Show all your work.

2. Submit this part to your Learning Coach for a grade.

Student Guide

Extended Problems: Reasoning

In this lesson, you'll complete Extended Problems: Reasoning for The Basics unit.

Goals for This Lesson
- Analyze complex problems using mathematical knowledge and skills.

Graded Activities in This Lesson
Extended Problems Graded Assignment

Extended Problems Graded Assignment [offline]

You will complete a graded assignment that focuses on reasoning in math.

Your learning coach will score this assignment.

- **Complete** the assignment on your own.
- **Submit** the completed assignment to your learning coach.

Student Guide

Systems of Linear Equations

Suppose movie tickets for adults cost $9 each, and tickets for children cost $5. A movie theater sells 284 tickets for a show for a total of $2164. How many adult tickets and how many children's tickets did the theater sell?

You can use two equations with two variables to solve this kind of problem..In this lesson, you will learn how to identify solutions to systems of linear equations

Goals for This Lesson
- Determine whether an ordered pair is a solution to a system of linear equations.

Graded Activities in This Lesson
Lesson Quiz (computer-scored)

Materials
Intermediate Mathematics C: A Reference Guide and Problem Sets, pages 171–173

Optional
calculator

Keywords
solution of a system of linear equations: an ordered pair that makes all of the equations in the system true

system of linear equations: two or more linear equations with the same variables

Groundwork: Preparing for the Lesson [online]
You will determine whether sets of ordered pairs are solutions to equations in two variables.

Learn: Solutions to Systems of Linear Equations [online]
You will learn how to test whether an ordered pair is a solution to a system of linear equations.

Summarize what you learned in this activity.
1. What is a system of linear equations?

2. What must be true about an ordered pair in order for it to be a solution to a system of equations?

Worked Examples: Solutions to Systems of Linear Equations [online]

Use the space below to work through the examples you see in the online screens.

Summary: Systems of Linear Equations [online]

A system of linear equations is two or more linear equations that use the same variables. A solution to a system of linear equations is an ordered pair that makes all of the equations in the system true. Graphically, the solution to a system of linear equations is the point, or points, where all lines in the system intersect.

Offline Learning: Systems of Linear Equations [offline]

Read pages 171–172 in the reference guide.

Problem Sets

Complete Problems 1–10 on pages 172–173.

Lesson Assessment: Systems of Linear Equations Quiz [online]

Go back online to complete the Lesson Quiz.

Student Guide

Solving Systems Using Inspection

Solutions to systems of linear equations are ordered pairs (x, y). Graphically, a solution to a linear system is a point where the graphs of the equations intersect. So how many solutions do linear systems of equations have? Are you tempted to say that they have only one solution? That answer is true some of the time, but not all of the time. In this lesson, you will learn how to determine the number of solutions there are to a system of linear equations, and you will learn how to classify systems.

Goals for This Lesson

- Use a graph to determine whether a system of linear equations will have 0, 1, or an infinite number of solutions.

- Classify systems of equations as inconsistent, consistent independent, or coincident (also called consistent dependent).

Graded Activities in This Lesson
Lesson Quiz (computer-scored)

Materials
Intermediate Mathematics C: A Reference Guide and Problem Sets, pages 174–177

Keywords
coincident system of equations: a consistent system of equations with infinitely many solutions; also known as a consistent dependent system

consistent system of equations: having at least one solution in common (the system has a nonempty solution set)

dependent system of equations: a consistent system of equations with infinitely many solutions; also known as coincident

equivalent equations: equations that have the same solution

inconsistent system of equations: a system of equations with no solution

independent system of equations: a consistent system of equations with exactly one solution

solution of a system of linear equations: an ordered pair that makes all of the equations in the system true

system of equations: two or more equations that contain the same variables

system of linear equations: two or more linear equations with the same variables

Learn: Classifying Systems from Graphs [online]

You will learn how to examine graphs of systems of linear equations in order to classify systems as consistent independent, coincident, or inconsistent. You will also determine whether systems have one solution, no solution, or infinitely many solutions.

Summarize what you learned in this activity.

1. What does it mean for a system to be consistent independent?

2. What does the graph of a consistent independent system look like?

3. What does it mean for a system to be coincident?

4. What does the graph of a coincident system look like?

5. What does it mean for a system to be inconsistent?

6. What does the graph of an inconsistent system look like?

Worked Examples: Classifying Systems from Graphs [online]

Use the space below to work through the examples you see in the online screens.

Learn: Classifying Systems by Inspection [online]

You will learn how to inspect systems of equations in order to classify them as consistent independent, coincident, or inconsistent.

Summarize what you learned in this activity.

1. When the equations of a linear system are in standard form, how would you classify the system if one equation were a multiple of the other equation?

2. When the equations of a linear system are in standard form, how would you classify the system if the sides of the equations containing the variables were the same, but the sides containing the constants were different?

3. When the equations of a linear system are in standard form, how would you classify the system if the sides of the equations containing the variables were different and neither equation was a multiple of the other equation?

Worked Examples: Classifying Systems by Inspection [online]

Use the space below to work through the examples you see in the online screens.

Summary: Solving Systems Using Inspection [online]

A solution to a system of linear equations is any ordered pair of numbers that makes all of the equations in the system true.

On a graph, the solution to a system is any point where the equations' lines intersect. You can classify a system as inconsistent (no solution), consistent independent (one solution), or consistent dependent (infinite solutions). A consistent dependent system is also called coincident.

You can also classify systems and determine the number of solutions by simply inspecting the equations in the system. To do this, first write the system equations in the same form, either standard form or slope-intercept form. Once the equations are in the same form, compare the equations' features to identify the type of system and the number of solutions.

Offline Learning: Solving Systems Using Inspection [offline]

Read pages 174–176 in the reference guide.

Problem Sets

Complete Problems 1–12 on pages 176–177.

Lesson Assessment: Solving Systems Using Inspection

Quiz [online]

Go back online to complete the Lesson Quiz.

Student Guide

Using Graphs to Solve Systems

Solutions to a linear equation in two variables are the ordered pairs of the points that graph the equation's line. Solutions to a system of linear equations are the ordered pairs of points that the equations share. In this lesson, you will learn how to use the graphing method to solve systems of equations.

Goals for This Lesson
- Use a graph to solve a system of linear equations.

- Use a graph to estimate the solution to a system of linear equations.

Graded Activities in This Lesson
Lesson Quiz (computer-scored)

Materials
Intermediate Mathematics C: A Reference Guide and Problem Sets, pages 178–181

Optional
calculator

Keywords
none

Groundwork: Preparing for the Lesson [online]
You will graph lines for equations that are in slope-intercept form.

Directions for using the Graphing Learning Tool:

1. Enter the equation $y = 3x + 2$ by typing it at the bottom of the screen.
2. Set the sliders for the first point to plot the *y*-intercept.
3. Starting at the point you just plotted, use the slope to find one more point on the line. Use the sliders for the second point to plot the point you identify.
4. Select Check.

5. If your line is correct, select Reset and then repeat Steps 1–4 for the equation $y = \frac{2}{3}x + 6$. If your line is incorrect, try again, or click Show Me.

Learn: The Graphing Method [online]

You will learn how to solve systems of linear equations by graphing.

Summarize what you learned in this activity.

1. What form should all of the equations of a system be in before you graph them?

2. What is the solution to a system of equations on a graph?

Worked Examples: The Graphing Method [online]

Use the space below to work through the examples you see in the online screens.

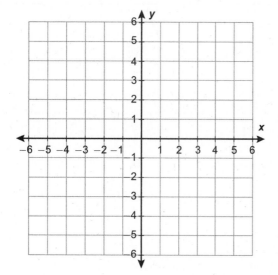

MathCast: Solving a System [online]

View the video to see how to solve a typical problem.

Summary: Using Graphs to Solve Systems [online]

To solve a system of equations by graphing, graph each equation in the system and look for the point of intersection. If the point of intersection does not have integer coordinates, you can estimate with the nearest point whose x- and y-coordinates are integers.

Offline Learning: Using Graphs to Solve Systems [offline]

Read pages 178–179 in the reference guide.

Problem Sets

Complete Problems 1–17 odd on pages 180–181.

Extra Practice (optional)

Complete Problems 2–18 even on pages 180–181.

Lesson Assessment: Using Graphs to Solve Systems

Quiz [online]

Go back online to complete the Lesson Quiz.

Student Guide

Substitution Method

Need sugar? Some people like it in their food but want to remain healthy, so they use one of the many sugar substitutes that are available. In the same way, suppose someone asks you to represent the number 6 in six different ways. You could probably come up with more than just six ways in almost no time:

$$(4 + 2),\ \frac{60}{10},\ \sqrt{36},\ \text{a half-dozen, the whole number between 5 and 7,}\ \frac{4 \cdot 12}{8},\ \text{and so on.}$$

If you wanted to refer to the number 6, you could use any one of these *substitutes* because they all equal 6. Substitution is the basis of another method for solving systems of linear equations.

Goals for This Lesson

- Use substitution to solve a system of linear equations.

Graded Activities in This Lesson

Lesson Quiz (computer-scored)

Materials

Intermediate Mathematics C: A Reference Guide and Problem Sets, pages 182–186

Optional

calculator

Keywords and Pronunciation

substitution method: solving systems of equations by replacing one variable or variable expression with another that is equal to it

Skills Update: Practice Your Math Skills [online]

Complete the Skills Update online.

Groundwork: Preparing for the Lesson [online]

You will review how to solve equations in two variables.

Learn: Substitute It! [online]

You will learn to use an algebraic method for solving systems of equations rather than using graphing. This method is called the substitution method.

Summarize what you learned in this activity.

1. List the steps for solving a system of equations using the substitution method.

2. Solve the following system of equations:

$$x + 5y = 7$$
$$2x + 4y = -4$$

3. When using the substitution method, how do you recognize an inconsistent system?

4. When using the substitution method, how do you recognize a coincident system?

Worked Examples: Try Substituting It [online]

Use the space below to work through the examples you see in the online screens.

MathCast: Substitution Method [online]

View the video to see how to solve a typical problem.

Summary: Substitution Method [online]

The substitution method is an algebraic method of solving a system of equations. It is more reliable, and often quicker, than the graphing method.

To use the substitution method, isolate a variable in either equation, substitute its equivalent expression into the other equation, and solve for the other variable. Then substitute that value into either equation and solve for the remaining variable.

Offline Learning: Substitution Method [offline]

Read pages 182–185 in the reference guide.

Problem Sets

Complete Problems 1–27 odd on pages 185–186.

Extra Practice (optional)
Complete Problems 2–26 even on pages 185–186.

Lesson Assessment: Substitution Method Quiz [online]

Now go back online to complete the Lesson Quiz.

Student Guide

Core Focus: Solving a System from Points

You've seen linear systems expressed as two or more equations and as graphs of two or more lines. Linear systems can also be expressed as two or more sets of points. In this lesson, you will learn how to determine the number of solutions to a linear system from two sets of points.

Goals for This Lesson
- Find the intersection of two lines given two points on each line.
- Write the equation of a line given a set of points on the line.
- Determine whether a system of equations has 0, 1, or infinitely many solutions.

Graded Activities in This Lesson
Lesson Quiz (computer-graded)

Materials
Intermediate Mathematics C: A Reference Guide and Problem Sets, pages 187–189

Optional
calculator

Keywords and Pronunciation
none

Groundwork: Preparing for the Lesson [online]
You will create systems of equations that are consistent independent, coincident, or inconsistent.

Learn: Solving a System from Points [offline]
Use the space below to take notes during this activity.

Overview

Solving a System from Points

Summary

Worked Examples: Solving a System from Points [online]
Use the space below to work through the examples you see in the online screens.

Offline Learning: Core Focus: Solving a System from Points

[offline]
Read pages 187–189.

Problem Sets
Complete Problems 1–6 on page 189.

Lesson Assessment: Core Focus: Solving a System from Points Quiz [online]

Go back online to complete the Lesson Quiz.

Student Guide

Applications: Systems of Linear Equations

The world is full of problems that involve two variables—investments, motion, mixtures, manufacturing, consumer purchases, and income, to name only a few. All can call for systems of equations in two variables. You have already practiced some strategies for solving such problems. In this lesson, you will apply your knowledge of systems of equations to real-world problem solving.

Goals for This Lesson
* Write a system of linear equations to solve a word problem.
* Solve a word problem using a system of linear equations.

Graded Activities in This Lesson
Lesson Quiz (computer-scored)

Materials
Intermediate Mathematics C: A Reference Guide and Problem Sets, pages 190–193

Optional
calculator

Skills Update: Practice Your Math Skills [online]
Complete the Skills Update online.

Learn: Modeling and Solving [online]
You will learn how to use systems of equations to solve real-world problems.

Summarize what you learned in this activity.

Write the system of equations that you can use to solve the problem.

1. The manager of a small theater knows that she sold 600 tickets in one evening, for a total of $1900. Adult tickets cost $4 each and children's tickets cost $2 each. How many of each type of ticket were sold?

Worked Examples: Try Modeling and Solving [online]

Use the space below to work through the examples you see in the online screens.

MathCast: Craft Shop [online]

View the video to see how to solve a typical problem.

Summary: Applications: Systems of Linear Equations [online]

If a real-world situation involves two unknowns and you have two facts, such as their total cost and their total value, or their total length and how they are related, then you can write a system of equations to solve for the unknowns.

Offline Learning: Applications: Systems of Linear Equations [offline]

Read pages 190–192 in the reference guide.

Problem Sets

Complete Problems 1–15 odd on pages 192–193.

Extra Practice (optional)
Complete Problems 2–14 even and 16–17 on pages 192–193.

Lesson Assessment: Applications: Systems of Linear Equations Quiz [online]

Now go back online to complete the Lesson Quiz.

Student Guide

Core Focus: Applications of Linear Systems

Suppose you're comparing two cell phone plans. For one plan, you'll pay $30 per month plus $0.10 per minute of use. For another plan, you'll pay $25 plus $0.15 per minute of use. After how many months will you pay an equal amount with both plans? This type of problem can be modeled using a system of linear equations. In this lesson, you will learn to solve these types of problems.

Goals for This Lesson

- Write a system of linear equations to solve a word problem.

- Solve a word problem using a system of linear equations.

- Interpret the solution to a system of equations within the context of the real-world situation that the system models.

- Interpret the graph of a system of linear equations within the context of the real-world situation that the system models.

Graded Activities in This Lesson
Lesson Quiz (computer-graded)

Materials
Intermediate Mathematics B: A Reference Guide and Problem Sets, pages 194–196

Optional
calculator

Keywords and Pronunciation
none

Groundwork: Preparing for the Lesson [online]
You will write equations to model real-world situations.

Learn: Solving Real-World Problems with Linear Systems

[offline]
Use the space below to take notes during this activity.

Overview

More Applications of Systems

Summary

Worked Examples: Solving Real-World Problems with Linear Systems [online]

Use the space below to work through the examples you see in the online screens.

Offline Learning: Core Focus: Applications of Linear Systems [offline]

Read pages 194–195.

Problem Sets

Complete Problems 1–3 on page 196.

Lesson Assessment: Core Focus: Applications of Linear Systems Quiz [online]

Go back online to complete the Lesson Quiz.

Student Guide

Core Focus: Mixture Problems

Suppose you have a container of pure apple juice and a container of a cranberry and apple juice mixture that has 40% cranberry juice and 60% apple juice. You want to combine the pure apple juice and the cranberry-apple juice mixture to create 4 cups of a new mixture that contains 80% apple juice. How much of each type of juice would you need to use? This type of problem is a mixture problem. Mixture problems involve combining products that contain percentages of a particular ingredient. You use systems of linear equations to solve them. In this lesson, you will learn how to solve mixture problems.

Goals for This Lesson
- Solve mixture problems.

Graded Activities in This Lesson
There is no graded activity associated with this lesson.

Materials
Intermediate Mathematics C: A Reference Guide and Problem Sets, pages 197–199

Optional
calculator

Keywords and Pronunciation
none

Learn: Mixture Problems [online]
Use the space below to take notes during this activity.

Overview

Solving Mixture Problems

Summary

Offline Learning: Core Focus: Mixture Problems [offline]
Read pages 197–199.

Problem Sets
Complete Problems 1–3 on pages 197–199.

Student Guide

Unit Review

In this unit, you have learned how to solve systems of linear equations graphically and by using the substitution method. You have learned how to classify systems as consistent independent, coincident, or inconsistent, and you have learned how to solve real-world problems involving systems of equations. Now it's time to pull together what you have learned.

Goals for This Lesson

- Determine whether an ordered pair is a solution to a system of linear equations.

- Use a graph to determine whether a system of linear equations will have 0, 1, or an infinite number of solutions.

- Classify systems of equations as inconsistent, consistent independent, or coincident (also called consistent dependent).

- Use a graph to solve a system of linear equations.

- Use a graph to estimate the solution to a system of linear equations.

- Use substitution to solve a system of linear equations.

- Find the intersection of two lines given two points on each line.

- Write the equation of a line given a set of points on the line.

- Determine whether a system of equations has 0, 1, or infinitely many solutions.

- Write a system of linear equations to solve a word problem.

- Solve a word problem using a system of linear equations.

- Interpret the solution to a system of equations within the context of the real-world situation that the system models.

- Interpret the graph of a system of linear equations within the context of the real-world situation that the system models.

- Solve mixture problems.

Graded Activities in This Lesson

There is no graded activity associated with this lesson.

Materials

Intermediate Mathematics C: A Reference Guide and Problem Sets, pages 200–201

Optional

Keywords

coincident system of equations: a consistent system of equations with infinitely many solutions; also known as a consistent dependent system

consistent system of equations: having at least one solution in common (the system has a nonempty solution set)

dependent system of equations: a consistent system of equations with infinitely many solutions; also known as coincident

equivalent equations: equations that have the same solution

inconsistent system of equations: a system of equations with no solution

independent system of equations: a consistent system of equations with exactly one solution

system of linear equations: two or more linear equations with the same variables

solution of a system of linear equations: an ordered pair that makes all of the equations in the system true

solution of an equation with two variables: an ordered pair of numbers that make a sentence true

Unit Review: Practice Test [online]

The last screen of the Practice Quiz will show you how many times you attempted each problem. For each problem, record your number of attempts below. Complete the activities and reference guide problems that correspond with the Practice Quiz problems that took you more than one attempt. Check off the review activities and review problems as you complete them.

Problem 1
Attempts: _____
□ Complete review activities online
□ Complete Problems 1–7 on pages 172–173

Problem 2
Attempts: _____
□ Complete review activities online
□ Complete Problems 1–4 on pages 176–177

Problem 3
Attempts: _____
□ Complete review activities online
□ Complete Problems 1–4 on pages 176–177

Problem 4
Attempts: _____
□ Complete review activities online
□ Complete Problems 1–4 on pages 176–177

Problem 5
Attempts: _____
□ Complete review activities online
□ Complete Problems 1–4 on page 180

Problem 6
Attempts: _____
□ Complete review activities online
□ Complete Problems 5–12 on page 177

Problem 7
Attempts: _____
□ Complete review activities online
□ Complete Problems 5–12 on page 177

Problem 8

Attempts: _____

☐ Complete review activities online

☐ Complete Problems 1–6 on page 189

Problem 9

Attempts: _____

☐ Complete review activities online

☐ Complete Problem 2 on page 192

Problem 10

Attempts: _____

☐ Complete review activities online

☐ Complete Problems 1–3 on page 199

Offline Learning: Systems of Equations Review [online]

Complete all the Chapter Review problems on pages 200–201. Use the Topic Lookup at the bottom of page 201 to review topics for any problems that were difficult for you.

Student Guide

Unit Test

You have learned to solve systems of linear equations graphically and by using the substitution method. You have learned how to classify systems as consistent independent, coincident, or inconsistent, and you have learned how to solve real-world problems involving systems of equations. Now it's time to take the Unit Test.

This Unit Test has two parts—one part that will be scored by the computer and one part that your Learning Coach will score. You will complete the computer-scored part first.

Goals for This Lesson
- Use a graph to solve a system of linear equations.

- Use substitution to solve a system of linear equations.

- Graph a system of two linear equations in two variables.

- Write a system of linear equations to solve a word problem.

- Solve a word problem using a system of linear equations.

- Solve mixture problems.

- Use linear combination to solve a system of equations.

- Determine whether a system of linear equations will have 0, 1, or an infinite number of solutions.

- Select and use an appropriate method to solve a system of linear equations.

- Write a system of linear equations to solve a word problem.

- Solve a word problem involving a system of equations.

- Classify systems of equations as inconsistent, consistent independent, or coincident (also called consistent dependent).

- Use a graph to estimate the solution to a system of linear equations.

- Write the equation of a line given a set of points on the line.

- Interpret the solution to a system of equations within the context of the real-world situation that the system models.

Graded Activities in This Lesson
Systems of Equations Test, Part 1

Systems of Equations Test, Part 2

Unit Assessment: Systems of Equations Test, Part 1 [online]
You will complete a test covering the main goals of this unit. This part of the test is online. It will be scored by the computer

---

Unit Assessment: Systems of Equations Test, Part 2 [offline]

This part of the Unit Test is offline.

1. Complete each question on your own. Show all your work.

2. Submit this part to your Learning Coach for a grade.

Student Guide

Extended Problems: Reasoning

In this lesson, you'll complete Extended Problems: Reasoning for the Systems of Equations unit.

Goals for This Lesson
- Analyze complex problems using mathematical knowledge and skills.

Graded Activities in This Lesson
Extended Problems: Reasoning

Extended Problems: Reasoning [offline]
You will complete a graded assignment that focuses on reasoning in math.

Your Learning Coach will score this assignment.

- **Complete** the assignment on your own.
- **Submit** the completed assignment to your Learning Coach.

Student Guide

Relations

Our universe contains an infinite set of points. That's a mind-boggling thought, especially when you consider that the head of a pin also contains an infinite set of points. Mathematicians try to get a grip on at least some of these points by mapping them with coordinates. This lesson deals with the way coordinates, or ordered pairs, relate to each other in a coordinate plane.

Goals for This Lesson

- Represent a relation with an arrow diagram, table, or graph.

- Find the domain and range for a relation or function.

Graded Activities in This Lesson
Lesson Quiz (computer-scored)

Materials
Intermediate Mathematics C: A Reference Guide and Problem Sets, pages 207–209

Optional
calculator

Keywords
domain: in a relation, the set of allowable inputs

range: in a relation the set of possible outputs

relation: a mapping from a set of inputs to a set of outputs

Groundwork: Preparing for the Lesson [online]
You will review how to plot points in a coordinate plane.

Learn: Representing a Relation [online]
You will learn different techniques for displaying relations.

Summarize what you learned in this activity.
1. Name four ways you can represent a relation with a finite (not infinite) number of input and output values.

Worked Examples: Try Representing a Relation [online]

Use the space below to work through the examples you see in the online screens.

Learn: Finding Domain and Range [online]

You will learn how to identify any relation's domain and range.

Summarize what you learned in this activity.

1. Tell how to find the domain and range of a relation in each format:

    - set of ordered pairs

    - table

    - arrow diagram

    - graph

Worked Examples: Try Finding Domain and Range [online]

Use the space below to work through the examples you see in the online screens.

Summary: Relations [online]

A relation is any set of ordered pairs where the set of first coordinates defines the domain and the set of second coordinates defines the range.

You can display a relation in a table, an arrow diagram, or a graph.

Offline Learning: Relations [offline]

Read pages 207–208 in the reference guide.

Problem Sets

Complete Problems 1–21 odd on pages 208–209.

Extra Practice (optional)
Complete Problems 2–22 even on pages 208–209.

Lesson Assessment: Relations Quiz [online]

Go back online to complete the Lesson Quiz.

Student Guide

Functions, Part 1

When you place whole coffee beans into an electric coffee grinder and turn on the grinder, in a few moments you will have ground coffee. Your input is whole coffee beans; your output is ground coffee. Functions act in a similar way. If you input a value into a function and perform its operations correctly, the result is an answer called the output.

Goals for This Lesson

- Determine whether a relation is a function.

Graded Activities in This Lesson

Lesson Quiz (computer-scored)

Materials

Intermediate Mathematics C: A Reference Guide and Problem Sets, pages 210–211, 213–214

Optional
calculator

Keywords

function: a relation that assigns each member of the domain to exactly one member of the range

Skills Update: Practice Your Math Skills [online]

Complete the Skills Update online.

Groundwork: Preparing for the Lesson [online]

You will review relations using a table, an arrow diagram, and a graph.

Learn: Functions [online]

You will learn about a special type of relation called a function.

Summarize what you learned in this activity.
1. What makes a relation a function?

2. Give an example of a relation that is a function and one that is not a function.

3. What is the vertical line test?

MathCast: Identifying Functions [online]
View the video to see how to solve a typical problem.

Worked Examples: Try Functions [online]
Use the space below to work through the examples you see in the online screens.

Summary: Functions, Part 1 [online]
A relation is a function if every input value is paired to exactly one output value. You can use the vertical line test to help determine if a graphed relation is a function.

Offline Learning: Functions, Part 1 [offline]
Read pages 210–211 in the reference guide.

Problem Sets
Complete Problems 1–12 on pages 213–214.

Lesson Assessment: Functions, Part 1 Quiz [online]
Go back online to complete the Lesson Quiz.

Student Guide

Functions, Part 2

Have you ever seen a kiosk that gives you cash for coins? Typically, you pour your coins into a machine, which adds the value of the coins and then subtracts a small service fee. When the process is complete, the machine prints out a receipt with the amount you can redeem for paper currency. The machine evaluates the value of the output (the receipt) based on the value of the input (the coins).

In this lesson, you will evaluate functions by finding the value of the output based on the value of a given input.

Goals for This Lesson
- Evaluate a function at a given point when given a graph or table.

Graded Activities in This Lesson
Lesson Quiz (computer-scored)

Materials
Intermediate Mathematics C: A Reference Guide and Problem Sets, pages 212–215

Optional
calculator

Groundwork: Preparing for the Lesson [online]
You will review relations using a table, an arrow diagram, and a graph.

Learn: Evaluating Functions [online]
You will learn how to evaluate a function

Summarize what you learned in this activity.
1. What does it mean to evaluate a function?

2. Describe how you would evaluate a function represented by
   - an equation

   - a set of ordered pairs

- a table

- a graph

Worked Examples: Try Evaluating Functions [online]
Use the space below to work through the examples you see in the online screens.

Summary: Functions, Part 2 [online]
To evaluate a function, find the output value for a given input value.

You can evaluate functions that are represented in different ways, including equations, sets of ordered pairs, tables, and graphs.

Offline Learning: Functions, Part 2 [offline]
Read pages 212–213 in the reference guide.

Problem Sets
Complete Problems 13–22 on pages 214–215.

Lesson Assessment: Functions, Part 2 Quiz [online]
Go back online to complete the Lesson Quiz.

Student Guide

Function Equations, Part 1

Functions give a name to the process of evaluating an expression. Let's continue your study of functions. In this lesson, you will compare different functions and talk about their properties. You will apply mathematical operations to functions and create new ones. Let's see how powerful this mathematical concept is.

Goals for This Lesson
* Write the equation of a linear function when given the graph.

Graded Activities in This Lesson
Lesson Quiz (computer-scored)

Materials
Intermediate Mathematics C: A Reference Guide and Problem Sets, pages 217–219

Optional
calculator

Keywords
dependent variable: the output variable for a function
independent variable: the input variable for a function
point -slope form: an equation of a line that passes through the points (x, y), has a slope m, and is given by $y - y_1 = m(x - x_1)$
slope-intercept form of an equation of a line: the equation of a line in the form $y = mx + b$, where m is the slope and b is the y-intercept

Groundwork: Preparing for the Lesson [online]
You will review how to write an equation from a graph.

Learn: Functions [online]
You will learn about writing functions as equations. In addition, you will write equations given a graph.

Summarize what you learned in this activity.
1. What is a dependent variable?

2. What is an independent variable?

3. What are the steps for writing the equation of a function from a graph?

Worked Examples: Function Equations, Part 1 [online]
Use the space below to work through the examples you see in the online screens.

Summary: Function Equations, Part 1 [online]
In a function equation, one variable is the dependent variable and the other is the independent variable.

To write the equation for a linear function from a graph,
- Determine the slope of the line.
- Identify one point on the line.

If you can identify the *y*-intercept, use that point to write the equation in slope-intercept form. Otherwise, use any point on the line to write the equation in point-slope form.

Offline Learning: Function Equations, Part 1 [offline]
Read page 217 in the reference guide.

Problem Sets
Complete Problems 1–8 on pages 218–219.

Lesson Assessment: Function Equations, Part 1 Quiz [online]
Go back online to complete the Lesson Quiz.

Student Guide

Function Equations, Part 2

If you have a job where you are paid by the hour, your pay is a function of the number of hours you work. The speed at which a race car moves is a function of the amount of pressure placed on the gas pedal. When one variable is a function of another, the relationship can be described with an equation.

Goals for This Lesson
- Calculate values for a function when given input values.

Graded Activities in This Lesson
Lesson Quiz (computer-scored)

Materials
Intermediate Mathematics C: A Reference Guide and Problem Sets, pages 218–221

Optional
calculator

Keywords
values of a function: members of the range of the function

Skills Update: Practice Your Math Skills [online]
Complete the Skills Update online.

Groundwork: Preparing for the Lesson [online]
You will review how to evaluate an expression.

Learn: Functions as Rules [online]
You will learn how to evaluate function equations to find values of the range for given values of the domain.

Summarize what you learned in this activity.
1. How do you evaluate a function equation for a given input value? Give an example.

Worked Examples: Try Functions as Rules [online]
Use the space below to work through the examples you see in the online screens.

Summary: Function Equations, Part 2 [online]
To evaluate a function equation, substitute the given value of the input variable into the function's rule and simplify.

Offline Learning: Function Equations, Part 2 [offline]
Read page 217–218 in the reference guide.

Problem Sets
Complete Problems 9–23 odd on pages 219–221.

Extra Practice (optional)
Complete Problems 10–22 even on pages 219–220.

Lesson Assessment: Function Equations, Part 2 Quiz [online]
Go back online to complete the Lesson Quiz.

Student Guide

Interpreting Function Graphs

Function graphs can have many different appearances. Some are straight lines, and some are curved or wavy. Some appear to rise from left to right, and some appear to fall. In this lesson, you will learn how to categorize and describe the behavior of functions based on the shapes of their graphs.

Goals for This Lesson
- Identify functions as linear or nonlinear based on information given in a table, graph, or equation.
- Determine whether a function is increasing, decreasing, or constant.

Graded Activities in This Lesson
Lesson Quiz (computer-scored)

Materials
Intermediate Mathematics C: A Reference Guide and Problem Sets, pages 222–227

Optional
calculator

Keywords
constant function: a function whose value does not increase or decrease as *x* increases

decreasing function: a function whose value decreases as *x* increases

increasing function: a function whose value increases as *x* increases

linear function: a function that when graphed forms a straight line

nonlinear function: a function that when graphed does not form a straight line

Learn: Linear vs. Nonlinear Functions [online]
You will learn how to determine whether a function is linear or nonlinear.

Summarize what you learned in this activity.
1. What is a linear function?

2. What is a nonlinear function?

Worked Examples: Linear vs. Nonlinear Functions [online]
Use the space below to work through the examples you see in the online screens.

Learn: Increasing, Decreasing, or Constant [online]
You will learn how to determine whether a function is increasing, decreasing, or constant.

Summarize what you learned in this activity.
1. What does it mean for a function to be increasing?

2. What does it mean for a function to be decreasing?

3. What does it mean for a function to be constant?

Worked Examples: Increasing, Decreasing, or Constant

[online]

Use the space below to work through the examples you see in the online screens.

Summary: Interpreting Function Graphs [online]

A linear function is a function whose graph is a straight line. A nonlinear function is a function whose graph is not a straight line.

Functions are increasing when they rise from left to right. Functions are decreasing when they fall from left to right. Functions are constant when they are horizontal.

Offline Learning: Interpreting Function Graphs [offline]

Read pages 222–225 in the reference guide.

Problem Sets

Complete Problems 1–20 on pages 225–227.

Lesson Assessment: Interpreting Function Graphs

Quiz [online]

Go back online to complete the Lesson Quiz.

Student Guide

Linear Function Models

Functions describe relationships between variables. Therefore, they model many real-world situations. When a function is linear, the slope and intercepts provide specific information about the real-world situation that the function represents. In this lesson, you will learn how to interpret and write function equations that model everyday situations.

Goals for This Lesson
- Write a linear function equation given two or more points.
- Write a linear function equation given a point and the slope.
- Interpret a linear function equation that models a real-world situation.
- Write a linear function equation that models a real-world situation.

Graded Activities in This Lesson
Lesson Quiz (computer-scored)

Materials
Intermediate Mathematics C: A Reference Guide and Problem Sets, pages 228–232

Optional
calculator

Keywords
rate of change: How fast a number changes compared to another number; for example, how much distance you cover in a certain amount of time

Learn: Writing Linear Function Equations [online]
You will write linear function equations given a point on the line and the line's slope, or given at least two points on the line.

Summarize what you learned in this activity.
1. What is the slope-intercept form of an equation?

2. What information do you need in order to write a linear function equation?

Worked Examples: Writing Linear Function Equations [online]

Use the space below to work through the examples you see in the online screens.

Learn: Interpreting and Writing Function Equations [online]

You will write linear function equations given a point on the line and the line's slope, or given at least two points on the line. You will also interpret the slope and intercepts of a function equation that models a real-world situation.

Summarize what you learned in this activity.

1. What is another name for the *y*-intercept?

2. What is the initial value of a function?

3. What part of a linear function equation is a rate of change?

Worked Examples: Interpreting and Writing Function Equations [online]

Use the space below to work through the examples you see in the online screens.

Summary: Linear Function Models [online]

You can use the slope formula and the slope-intercept form of the equation of a line to write a function equation.

When a linear function models a real-world situation, the *y*-intercept, also called the vertical intercept, is often the situation's starting value. The slope is the rate of change.

Offline Learning: Linear Function Models [offline]

Read pages 228–231 in the reference guide.

Problem Sets

Complete Problems 2–14 even and 16–20 on pages 231–232.

Extra Practice (optional)
Complete Problems 1–15 odd on pages 231–232.

Lesson Assessment: Linear Function Models Quiz [online]

Go back online to complete the Lesson Quiz.

Student Guide

Function Representations

Functions can be represented in different ways. They can appear as equations, as graphs, and as tables. Sometimes, you may need to compare functions, particularly when they model real-world situations. In this lesson, you will learn how to make meaningful comparisons between two functions.

Goals for This Lesson
- Compare properties of two functions when each is represented in a different way.

Graded Activities in This Lesson
Lesson Quiz (computer-scored)

Materials
Intermediate Mathematics C: A Reference Guide and Problem Sets, pages 233–239

Optional
calculator

Learn: Comparing Linear Functions [online]
You will compare linear functions that are represented as graphs, tables, or equations.

Summarize what you learned in this activity.
1. If you are asked to compare the rate of change of two linear functions, what must you find?

2. How can you determine which function has the greater rate of change if the slope of one or both functions is negative?

3. Besides the slopes, what other features of two functions can you compare?

Worked Examples: Try Comparing Linear Functions [online]
Use the space below to work through the examples you see in the online screens.

Summary: Function Representations [online]

To compare linear functions, compare their rates of change, or slope, and their intercepts.

Offline Learning: Function Representations [offline]

Read pages 233–236 in the reference guide.

Problem Sets

Complete Problems 1–18 on pages 237–239.

Lesson Assessment: Function Representations Quiz [online]

Go back online to complete the Lesson Quiz.

Student Guide

Core Focus: Functions

A function can represent a real-world situation. For instance, if you walk from your house to visit a friend and make some stops along the way, you can represent the distance you travel over time as a function. A graph of the function tells a story of your trip. In this lesson, you will use graphs to understand functions in real-world situations.

Goals for This Lesson

- Identify functions as linear or nonlinear based on information given in a table, graph, or equation.

- Determine whether a function is increasing, decreasing, or constant.

- Use the graph of a function to describe the relationship between two quantities.

Graded Activities in This Lesson
Lesson Quiz (computer-graded)

Materials
Intermediate Mathematics C: A Reference Guide and Problem Sets, pages 240–242

Optional
calculator

Groundwork: Preparing for the Lesson [online]
You will determine when a function is increasing, decreasing, or constant, using its graph.

Summarize what you learned in this activity.
1. How do you know a function is increasing or decreasing?

2. When is a function constant?

Learn: Functions in Real-World Situations [offline]
Use the space below to take notes during this activity.

Interpreting Functions

Summary

Worked Examples: Functions in Real-World Situations [online]

Use the space below to work through the examples you see in the online screens.

Offline Learning: Core Focus: Functions [offline]

Read pages 240–241.

Problem Sets

Complete Problems 1–9 on page 242.

Lesson Assessment: Core Focus: Functions Quiz [online]

Go back online to complete the Lesson Quiz.

Student Guide

Core Focus: Sketching Function Graphs

Sketch artists are able to draw faces based on a description. You may describe the shape or size of someone's facial features, and the artist can draw a picture that is very similar to that person's face. In the same way, you can use the description of a real-world situation to draw a picture—a picture that is the graph of a function.

Goals for This Lesson
- Sketch the graph of a function described in a word problem.

Graded Activities in This Lesson
There is no graded activity associated with this lesson.

Materials
Intermediate Mathematics C: A Reference Guide and Problem Sets, pages 243–245

Optional
calculator

Learn: Sketching Function Graphs [online]
Use the space below to take notes during this activity.

Overview

Function Graphs from Words

Summary

Offline Learning: Core Focus: Sketching Function Graphs [offline]
Read pages 243–245.

Problem Sets
Complete Problems 1–4 on page 245.

Student Guide

Unit Review

You have learned that functions are a one-to-one correspondence between the domain and the range. You have learned to evaluate functions, graph functions, analyze graphs of functions, and interpret and sketch functions in real-world situations. Now it's time to pull together what you have learned.

Goals for This Lesson

- Represent a relation with an arrow diagram, table, or graph.

- Find the domain and range for a relation or function.

- Determine whether a relation is a function.

- Evaluate a function at a given point when given a graph or table.

- Identify a function graph that best represents a real-world situation.

- Calculate values for a function when given input values.

- Identify functions as linear or nonlinear based on information given in a table, graph, or equation.

- Compare properties of two functions when each is represented in a different way.

- Determine whether a function is increasing, decreasing, or constant.

- Use the graph of a function to describe the relationship between two quantities.

- Write the equation of a linear function when given the graph.

- Write a linear function equation when given two or more points.

- Write a linear function equation when given a point and the slope.

- Interpret a linear function equation that models a real-world situation.

- Write a linear function equation that models a real-world situation.

- Sketch the graph of a function described in a word problem.

Graded Activities in This Lesson

There is no graded activity associated with this lesson.

Materials

Intermediate Mathematics C: A Reference Guide and Problem Sets, pages 246–247

Optional

calculator

Keywords

constant function: a function whose value does not increase or decrease as *x* increases

decreasing function: a function whose value decreases as *x* increases

dependent variable: the output variable for a function

domain of a function: the set of all input values for which a function is defined

function: a correspondence between two sets—the domain and the range—that assigns to each member of the domain exactly one member of the range

graph of a relation: the graphs of all the ordered pairs that form the relation

increasing function: a function whose value increases as x increases

independent variable: the input variable for a function

linear function: a function that when graphed forms a straight line

nonlinear function: a function that when graphed does not form a straight line

one-to-one correspondence: a function between two sets where each element in one set (the domain) corresponds to exactly one element in the other set (the range) and vice versa

point-slope form: an equation of a line that passes through the points (x, y), has a slope of m, and is given by $y - y_1 = m(x - x_1)$

range of a function: the set of all possible output values of a function

rate of change: how fast a number changes compared to another number; for example, how much distance you cover in a certain amount of time

slope-intercept form: the equation of a line in the form $y = mx + b$, where m is the slope and b is the y-intercept

Unit Review: Practice Test [online]

The last screen of the Practice Quiz will show you how many times you attempted each problem. For each problem, record your number of attempts below. Complete the activities and reference guide problems that correspond with the Practice Quiz problems that took you more than one attempt. Check off the review activities and review problems as you complete them.

Problem 1
Attempts: _____
□ Complete review activities online
□ Complete Problems 13–22 on page 209

Problem 2
Attempts: _____
□ Complete review activities online
□ Complete Problems 1–12 on pages 213–214

Problem 3
Attempts: _____
□ Complete review activities online
□ Complete Problems 13–20 on pages 214–215

Problem 4
Attempts: _____
□ Complete review activities online
□ Complete Problems 1–8 on pages 218–219

Problem 5
Attempts: _____
□ Complete review activities online
□ Complete Problems 15–20 on pages 226–227

Problem 6
Attempts: _____
☐ Complete review activities online
☐ Complete Problems 1–12 on page 231

Problem 7
Attempts: _____
☐ Complete review activities online
☐ Complete Problems 1–4 on page 237

Problem 8
Attempts: _____
☐ Complete review activities online
☐ Complete Problems 5–15 on pages 237–238

Problem 9
Attempts: _____
☐ Complete review activities online
☐ Complete Problems 1–8 on page 242

Problem 10
Attempts: _____
☐ Complete review activities online
☐ Complete Problems 1–4 on page 245

Offline Learning: Function Basics Review [online]

Complete all of the Chapter Review problems on pages 246–247. Use the Topic Lookup at the bottom of page 247 to review topics for any problems that were difficult for you.

Student Guide

Function Basics Test

You have learned to evaluate functions, graph functions, analyze graphs of functions, and interpret functions in real-world situations. Now it's time to take the Unit Test. This Unit Test has two parts—one part that will be scored by the computer and one part that your Learning Coach will score. You will complete the computer-scored part first.

Goals for This Lesson

- Find the domain and range for a relation or function.

- Determine whether a relation is a function.

- Evaluate a function at a given point when given a graph or table.

- Calculate values for a function when given input values.

- Identify functions as linear or nonlinear based on information given in a table, graph, or equation.

- Determine whether a function is increasing, decreasing, or constant.

- Write the equation of a linear function when given the graph.

- Write a linear function equation when given two or more points.

- Write a linear function equation given a point and the slope.

- Write a linear function equation that models a real-world situation.

- Compare properties of two functions when each is represented in a different way.

- Sketch the graph of a function described in a word problem.

Graded Activities in This Lesson

Function Basics Test, Part 1

Function Basics Test, Part 2

Unit Assessment: Function Basics Test, Part 1 [online]

This part of the Unit Test is online. It will be scored by the computer.

Unit Assessment: Function Basics Test, Part 2 [offline]

This part of the Unit Test is offline.

1. Complete each question on your own. Show all your work.

2. Submit this part to your Learning Coach for a grade.

Student Guide

Extended Problems: Real-World Application

In this lesson, you'll complete Extended Problems: Real-World Application for the Function Basics unit.

Goals for This Lesson
- Apply mathematical knowledge and skills to evaluate and analyze real-world situations.

Graded Activities in This Lesson
Extended Problems: Real-World Application

Extended Problems: Real-World Application [offline]
You will complete a graded assignment that focuses on a real-world application of math.

Your teacher will grade this assignment.

- **Save** the graded assignment to your computer. In the filename, replace "studentname" with your last name followed by your first initial.
- **Complete** the assignment on your own.
- **Submit** the completed assignment according to your teacher's instructions.

Student Guide

Semester Review

In this semester, you identified and combined like terms, simplified expressions involving positive and negative exponents, wrote numbers in scientific notation, and estimated and compared very large or very small numbers. You solved equations, which led to graphing points and lines, finding intercepts, and determining and interpreting slopes. You learned various ways to write the equation of a line.

You learned how to solve systems of equations by graphing and by substitution. You classified systems as consistent independent, coincident, or inconsistent. You also evaluated, graphed, analyzed, and interpreted functions. Throughout the semester, you applied what you learned to real-world problems.

Goals for This Lesson
- Review the concepts and skills learned in the semester.

Graded Activities in This Lesson
There is no graded activity associated with this lesson.

Materials
Intermediate Mathematics C: A Reference Guide and Problem Sets

Optional

calculator

Keywords
bases: a number that is raised to some power (for example, in 5^3, 5 is the base)

coincident system of equations: a consistent system of equations with infinitely many solutions; also known as a consistent dependent system

collinear: three or more points are collinear if a straight line can be drawn through the given points

consistent system of equations: having at least one solution in common (the system has a nonempty solution set)

constant function: a function whose value does not increase or decrease as *x* increases

contradiction: an equation that is true for no values of the variable

coordinate axes: the *x*- and *y*-axes in a coordinate plane

coordinates of a point: the *x*- and *y*-coordinates of a point, written as an ordered pair of numbers

decreasing function: a function whose value decreases as *x* increases

dependent system of equations: a consistent system of equations with infinitely many solutions; also known as coincident

dependent variable: the output variable for a function

domain of a function: the set of all input values for which a function is defined

empty set: the set with no elements, also known as the null set

equivalent equations: equations that have the same solution

function: a correspondence between two sets—the domain and the range—that assigns to each member of the domain exactly one member of the range

graph of a relation: the graphs of all the ordered pairs that form the relation

graph of an ordered pair: the point in a coordinate plane associated with an ordered pair of real numbers

grouping symbols: devices, such as parentheses, brackets, and fraction bars, used to set apart an expression that should be simplified before other operations are performed

identity: an equation that is true for any value of the variable

inconsistent system of equations: a system of equations with no solution

increasing function: a function whose value increases as x increases

independent system of equations: a consistent system of equations with exactly one solution

independent variable: the input variable for a function

initial amount: the beginning value of a linear relationship before any time has passed; the initial amount, also known as initial value, is the y-intercept of the line

inverse operations: mathematical operations that undo each other, such as addition and subtraction or multiplication and division

linear function: a function that when graphed forms a straight line

nonlinear function: a function that when graphed does not form a straight line

one-to-one correspondence: a function between two sets where each element in one set (the domain) corresponds to exactly one element in the other set (the range) and vice versa

order-of-magnitude estimate: a calculation that provides an answer that is accurate to the nearest power of 10

ordered pair of numbers: two numbers, where the first number represents a value on the horizontal axis, and the second number represents a value on the vertical axis, such as (x, y)

origin: the intersection of the axes on a coordinate plane; the point $(0, 0)$

plot a point: locate the graph of an ordered pair of real numbers in a coordinate plane

point-slope form: an equation of a line that passes through the points (x, y), has a slope of m, and is given by $y - y_1 = m(x - x_1)$

power of a number: the product when a number is multiplied by itself a given number of times (e.g., 5^3 is the third power of five)

proportional relationship: a relationship that can be described by an equation of the form $y = kx$, where k is the constant of proportionality

quadrant: one of the four regions into which the coordinate axes separate the coordinate plane

range of a function: the set of all possible output values of a function

rate: a ratio that compares quantities of different kinds of units

rate of change: the rate at which quantities change over time in a linear relationship; the rate of change is the slope of the line

slope: a number that describes the steepness of a line, computed as the ratio of the change in the y-coordinates to the change in the x-coordinates when moving from one point on a line to another point on the same line

slope-intercept form of an equation of a line: the equation of a line in the form $y = mx + b$, where m is the slope and b is the y-intercept

solution of a system of linear equations: an ordered pair that makes all of the equations in the system true

solution of an equation with two variables: an ordered pair of numbers that make a sentence true

solution set of an equation: the set of all solutions of an equation

standard form of a linear equation: $Ax + By = C$, where A, B, and C are integers and A and B are not both zero

system of linear equations: two or more linear equations with the same variables

transform an equation: to rewrite an equation or inequality as an equivalent equation or inequality

transformation: an operation performed on an equation or an inequality that produces a simpler equivalent statement

transformation by addition: adding the same real number to each side of a given equation or inequality

transformation by division: dividing each side of a given equation by the same nonzero real number

transformation by multiplication: multiplying each side of a given equation by the same nonzero real number

transformation by substitution: replacing any expression in a given equation or inequality with an equivalent expression

transformation by subtraction: subtracting the same real number from each side of a given equation

unit rate: a rate that has a denominator of 1

x-axis: the horizontal number line in a coordinate plane

y-axis: the vertical number line in a coordinate plane

x-intercept: the x-coordinate of a point where a graph intersects the x-axis

y-intercept: the y-coordinate of a point where a graph intersects the y-axis

Semester Review: Look Back at the Semester [online]
You will review key concepts from the semester to prepare for the Semester Test.

Offline Learning: Prepare for the Semester Test [offline]

Complete the following problems:

- Problems 1–9 odd and 12–24 even on pages 40–41
- Problems 1–9 odd and 14–26 even on pages 76–77
- Problems 1–13 odd and 14 on pages 126–127
- Problems 1–13 odd on pages 164–165
- Problems 1–15 odd on pages 200–201
- Problems 1–11 odd on pages 246–247

Use the Topic Lookups to review topics for any problems that were difficult for you.

Student Guide

Semester Test, Part 1

It's time to take the Semester Test. This Semester Test has two parts—one part that will be scored by the computer and one part that your Learning Coach will score. You will complete the computer-scored part in this lesson.

Goals for This Lesson

- Simplify a numerical expression without grouping symbols.
- Simplify a numerical expression with grouping symbols.
- Place grouping symbols in an expression to create a specific value.
- Identify like terms.
- Simplify an expression using the distributive property.
- Collect like terms.
- Simplify a numerical expression involving positive exponents.
- Evaluate a variable expression involving positive exponents.
- Write a number as a power of a given number.
- Simplify an expression involving negative exponents.
- Solve an equation involving negative exponents.
- Use the product of powers property to multiply powers.
- Use the quotient of powers property to divide powers.
- Use the power to a power property to raise a power to another power.
- Write a whole or decimal number using scientific notation.
- Write a number given in scientific notation as a whole or decimal number.
- Multiply, divide, add, and subtract numbers given in scientific notation.
- Estimate a quantity as a product of a single digit and a power of 10.
- Compare numbers that are expressed as the product of a single digit and a power of 10.
- Determine the best order-of-magnitude estimate for a number.
- Use dimensional analysis to convert units when quantities are expressed in scientific notation.
- Interpret numbers expressed in scientific notation on a calculator.
- For very large or very small numbers, determine the number of times greater one number is than another number.
- Solve addition or subtraction equations.
- Solve addition or subtraction equations involving simplification.
- Solve a word problem involving addition or subtraction.
- Write an equation that models a word problem involving addition or subtraction.
- Solve an equation involving division.

- Solve an equation involving multiplication.

- Write an equation that models a word problem involving multiplication or division.

- Solve a word problem that involves an equation with multiplication or division.

- Solve an equation involving more than one transformation.

- Write an equation to solve a word problem that involves an equation with multiple transformations.

- Solve an equation that has a variable on both sides.

- Solve word problems that involve equations with variables on both sides.

- Identify an equation as an identity, a contradiction, or neither.

- Determine whether given linear equations have one solution, no solutions, or infinite solutions.

- Create equations that have one solution, no solution, or infinite solutions.

- Solve equations involving rational coefficients.

- Solve an equation in two variables in terms of one of the variables.

- Determine whether or not an ordered pair is a solution to a given equation.

- Identify a point on a graph, given specific criteria.

- Graph a point when given an ordered pair.

- Identify the quadrant for a point on a graph.

- Write the equation of a line in standard form.

- Use a graph to determine if a set of points is collinear.

- Use intercepts to graph a linear equation on a coordinate plane.

- Determine whether a line has positive slope, negative slope, zero slope, or undefined slope.

- Find the slope of a line given two points.

- Find the slope of a line given the equation of the line.

- Derive the equation $y = mx$ for a line that passes through the origin.

- Identify coordinates on a line given an equation in the form $y = mx$.

- Graph equations of the form $y = mx$ by plotting points.

- Graph equations of the form $y = mx$ using the origin and the slope.

- Interpret a slope as a rate for a given problem context.

- Use a rate to model and solve problems.

- Use similar triangles to analyze the slope of a line.

- Compare two proportional relationships that are represented in different ways.

- Graph proportional relationships.

- Interpret the unit rate of a proportional relationship as the slope of a graph.

- Find the slope and y-intercept of a line when given its equation in slope-intercept form.

- Find the y-intercept of a line when given its equation in slope-intercept form.

- Transform an equation into slope-intercept form.

- Graph a line when its equation is given as or transformed into slope-intercept form.

- Write an equation of a line in point-slope form when given specific criteria or a graph.

- Solve a word problem using the point-slope form of an equation.

- Graph a line in point-slope form.

- Write an equation of a line in point-slope form when given specific criteria.

- Write an equation of a line in standard form when given specific criteria.

- Write an equation of a horizontal or vertical line.

- Write an equation of a line in slope-intercept form when given specific criteria.

- Calculate values for a linear equation in two variables.

- Determine if a word problem is modeled by a linear relationship or not.

- Write an equation in slope-intercept form to model a given word problem.

- Identify information that can be used to graph a line from a word problem describing a linear relationship.

- Sketch a graph that exhibits the qualitative features of a function that has been described verbally.

- Write an equation to represent a linear relationship described in a word problem.

- Interpret the rate of change and initial amount of a linear relationship described in a word problem.

- Use a graph to solve a system of linear equations.

- Use a graph to determine whether a system of linear equations will have 0, 1, or an infinite number of solutions.

- Use substitution to solve a system of linear equations.

- Write a system of linear equations to solve a word problem.

- Solve a word problem using a system of linear equations.

- Solve mixture problems.

- Determine whether an ordered pair is a solution to a system of linear equations.

- Find the intersection of two lines given two points on each line.

- Classify systems of equations as inconsistent, consistent independent, or coincident (also called consistent dependent).

- Use a graph to estimate the solution to a system of linear equations.

- Write the equation of a line given a set of points on the line.

- Determine whether a system of equations has 0, 1, or infinitely many solutions.

- Interpret the solution to a system of equations within the context of the real-world situation that the system models.

- Interpret the graph of a system of linear equations within the context of the real-world situation that the system models.

- Represent a relation with an arrow diagram, table, or graph.

- Find the domain and range for a relation or function.

- Determine whether a relation is a function.

- Evaluate a function at a given point when given a graph or table.

- Identify a function graph that best represents a real-world situation.

- Calculate values for a function when given input values.

- Identify functions as linear or nonlinear based on information given in a table, graph, or equation.

- Compare properties of two functions when each is represented in a different way.

- Determine whether a function is increasing, decreasing, or constant.

- Use the graph of a function to describe the relationship between two quantities.

- Write the equation of a linear function when given the graph.

- Write a linear function equation when given two or more points.

- Write a linear function equation when given a point and the slope.

- Interpret a linear function equation that models a real-world situation.

- Write a linear function equation that models a real-world situation.

- Sketch the graph of a function described in a word problem.

Graded Activities in This Lesson
Semester Test: Intermediate Mathematics C, Part 1

Semester Assessment: Intermediate Mathematics C, Part 1 Test [online]
You will complete a test covering the main goals of this semester. This part of the test is online. It will be scored by the computer.

Student Guide

Semester Test, Part 2

It's time to take the offline part of the Semester Test.

Goals for This Lesson

- Write a variable expression for a word problem.
- Solve a word problem using a system of linear equations.
- Determine whether a relation is a function.
- Determine the domain of a function when given ordered pairs or a table.
- Find the range for a function.
- Determine whether given linear equations have one solution, no solutions, or infinite solutions.
- Write an equation to represent a linear relationship described in a word problem.
- Determine the rate of change or specified values of a linear relationship described in a real-world context.
- Interpret the rate of change and initial amount of a linear relationship described in a word problem.

Graded Activities in This Lesson

Semester Test: Intermediate Mathematics C, Part 2

Semester Test: Intermediate Mathematics C, Part 2 [offline]

This part of the Semester Test is offline.

1. Complete each question on your own. Show all your work.
2. Submit this part to your Learning Coach for a grade.

Student Guide

Direct Linear Variation, Part 1

When you buy gas for a car, the amount you pay is based on the number of gallons you buy. If you buy twice as many gallons as your friend does, then you will pay twice as much as your friend does. If you buy three times as many gallons, then you will pay three times as much, and so on. This type of relationship is called a direct linear variation and is a special type of function.

Goals for This Lesson

- Find the constant of variation when given data for a function with direct linear variation.

- Solve a problem involving direct linear variation.

- Write a formula for a problem involving a direct linear variation.

Graded Activities in This Lesson
Lesson Quiz (computer-scored)

Materials
Intermediate Mathematics C: A Reference Guide and Problem Sets, pages 253–256

Optional
calculator

Keywords and Pronunciation
constant of variation: the nonzero constant k defined by $y = kx$ in a direct variation; also called the *constant of proportionality*

direct linear variation: a function where y varies directly with x following the equation $y = kx$, where k is a nonzero constant

Groundwork: Preparing for the Lesson [online]
You will review how to write and simplify ratios

Learn: Varying Directly [online]

You will learn about direct linear variation. You will learn the general equation for a direct linear variation, and you will learn to write a specific equation given certain criteria about a direct linear variation.

Summarize what you learned in this activity.

1. What is the general equation for a direct linear variation?

2. How do you find the constant of variation from a table of ordered pairs?

3. Describe the graph of a direct variation.

Worked Examples: Try Varying Directly [online]

Use the space below to work through the examples you see in the online screens.

Summary: Direct Linear Variation, Part 1 [online]

Some quantities vary directly with one another and are described by an equation in the form $y = kx$, where k is a nonzero constant of variation. The function that defines that equation is known as a direct variation or a direct linear variation.

Offline Learning: Direct Linear Variation, Part 1 [offline]
Read pages 253–255 in the reference guide.

Problem Sets
Complete Problems 1–21 odd on pages 255–256.

Lesson Assessment: Direct Linear Variation, Part 1 Quiz [online]
Go back online to complete the Lesson Quiz.

Student Guide

Direct Linear Variation, Part 2

Problems involving direct linear variation cover a wide range of fields, including construction, landscaping, architecture, manufacturing, business, banking, electronics, computers, and science. In this lesson, you will apply what you already know about direct variation to solving practical problems.

Goals for This Lesson
- Solve a problem involving direct variation.

Graded Activities in This Lesson
Lesson Quiz (computer-scored)

Materials
Intermediate Mathematics C: A Reference Guide and Problem Sets, pages 255–256

Optional
calculator

Keywords and Pronunciation
constant of variation: the nonzero constant k defined by $y = kx$ in a direct variation; also called the *constant of proportionality*

direct linear variation: a function where y varies directly with x following the equation $y = kx$, where k is a nonzero constant

Skills Update: Practice Your Math Skills [online]
Complete the Skills Update online.

Groundwork: Preparing for the Lesson [online]
You will review how to find the constant of variation in a direct linear variation problem.

Learn: Variety and Variation [online]
You will learn to solve real-world problems that involve direct linear variation. Use the space provided here to follow along with the online example.

1. Describe a relationship in your everyday life that can be modeled by a direct variation equation.

2. Outline a problem-solving plan for solving direct variation problems.

Worked Examples: Try Variety and Variation [online]

Use the space below to work through the examples you see in the online screens.

MathCast: Paychecks [online]

View the video to see how to solve a typical problem.

Summary: Direct Linear Variation, Part 2 [online]

Many quantities in the real world vary with one another. The relationship between two quantities is called a direct linear variation if it can be described by an equation in the form $y = kx$, where k is a nonzero constant of variation.

You can use your knowledge of direct relationships between variables to solve a variety of problems.

Offline Learning: Direct Linear Variation, Part 2 [offline]

Read page 255 in the reference guide.

Problem Sets

Complete Problems 23–28 on page 256.

Lesson Assessment: Direct Linear Variation, Part 2 Quiz [online]

Go back online to complete the Lesson Quiz.

Student Guide

Quadratic Variation

You've just learned about direct linear variation; however, not every relationship is linear. In this lesson, you are going to learn about another type of relationship called *quadratic variation*. As in the lessons on direct linear variation, you are going to learn the general equation for a quadratic variation. You will learn how to determine whether or not a relationship shows a quadratic variation, and you will learn how to graph a quadratic variation.

Goals for This Lesson
- Find the constant of variation when given data for a function with quadratic variation.
- Write a formula for a problem involving a quadratic variation.
- Solve a problem involving quadratic variation.
- Graph a function involving quadratic variation

Graded Activities in This Lesson
Lesson Quiz (computer-scored)

Materials
Intermediate Mathematics C: A Reference Guide and Problem Sets, pages 257–261

Optional
calculator
graph paper

Keywords and Pronunciation
quadratic variation: a relationship between x and y in which you can write the function describing the relationship in a form of the general equation $y = kx^2$, where k is a nonzero constant

Groundwork: Preparing for the Lesson [online]
You will review what you've already learned about direct linear variation to help you prepare for quadratic variation.

Learn: Identifying and Using Quadratic Variation [online]
You will learn the general equation for a quadratic variation, and you will learn how to determine whether relationships show a quadratic variation. You will also learn how to find the equation of a quadratic variation given only one set of corresponding x- and y-values.

Summarize what you learned in this activity.

1. What is the general equation for a quadratic variation, and how does it differ from the general equation for a direct linear variation?

2. How can you determine whether a set of *x*- and corresponding *y*-values show a quadratic variation relationship?

3. Describe how to find the equation of a quadratic variation given one *x*-value and the corresponding *y*-value.

Worked Examples: Try Identifying and Using Quadratic Variation

[online]
Use the space below to work through the examples you see in the online screens.

Learn: Graphing Quadratic Variation [online]

You will graph a quadratic variation.

Summarize what you learned in this activity.

1. Describe how you can graph a quadratic variation.

2. Describe the graph of any quadratic variation.

Worked Examples: Try Graphing Quadratic Variation [online]

Use the space below to work through the examples you see in the online screens.

Summary: Quadratic Variation [online]

If a relation is a quadratic variation, then each output is the product of the square of its input and a nonzero constant of variation, k, and can be described by an equation in the form $y = kx^2$. The graph of a quadratic variation is a U-shaped curve whose turning point lies at the origin.

Offline Learning: Quadratic Variation [offline]

Read pages 257–260 in the reference guide.

Problem Sets

Complete Problems 2–16 even and 17–25 odd on pages 260–261.

Lesson Assessment: Quadratic Variation Quiz [online]

Now go back online to complete the Lesson Quiz.

Student Guide

Patterns in Two-Way Tables

Data are collected and analyzed to solve problems and make decisions. One type of data is called categorical data. These data organize information in terms of groups or categories. For example, if you asked your friends whether they prefer pizza or hamburgers, the data collected from each friend would be either pizza or hamburgers, and not a measurement or amount. When you gather your friends' responses, you might want to further organize their answers into responses by boys and responses by girls. You might then use these two sets of categories (pizza versus hamburgers, and boys or girls) to draw conclusions on whether, among your friends, boys tend to like hamburgers or most of the girls prefer pizza. In this lesson, you will learn to create tables that organize categorical data and to use those tables to analyze the data.

Goals for This Lesson

- Construct and interpret a two-way table summarizing data on two categorical variables collected from the same subjects.

- Use relative frequencies calculated for rows or columns to describe possible association between bivariate categorical data.

Graded Activities in This Lesson
Lesson Quiz (computer-scored)

Materials
Intermediate Mathematics C: A Reference Guide and Problem Sets, pages 262–267

Optional

calculator

Keywords
association: the relationship between two variables

bivariate data: data that show the relationship between two variables; paired data

categorical variable: a variable that is separable into mutually exclusive groups (for example, boys and girls or athletes and nonathletes)

data: a collection of related facts; a collection of categorical or quantitative information

frequency: the number of observations within a range of data

relative frequency: The number of observations within a given class or category, divided by the total number of observations: $\dfrac{\#\ of\ observations\ within\ a\ class}{total\ \#\ of\ observations}$. If there is more than one class, each relative frequency will be less than 1, and all relative frequencies will add up to 1.

two-way table: a frequency table for two categorical variables

two-way relative frequency table: a table that shows the relative frequencies of each data value in a two-way table

quantitative variable: data that can be measured numerically

Groundwork: Preparing for the Lesson [online]

You will review the following terms to prepare for this lesson: data, quantitative variable, categorical variable, and frequency.

Learn: Creating a Two-Way Table [online]

You will create a two-way table and interpret the data for two categorical variables.

Summarize what you learned in this activity.

1. What are categorical variables?

2. What is a two-way table?

Learn: Interpreting Two-Way Tables [online]

You will calculate relative frequencies for categorical data and describe possible associations between the variables.

Summarize what you learned in this activity.

1. What is relative frequency?

2. What is an association between categorical variables?

3. How can relative frequencies help you determine whether there is an association between categorical variables?

Worked Examples: Try Creating and Interpreting Two-Way Tables [online]

Use the space below to work through the examples you see in the online screens.

Summary: Patterns in Two-Way Tables [online]

Categorical variables are variables whose data are named or categorized rather than measured. Bivariate categorical data consist of two categorical variables.

You can use a two-way table to compare bivariate categorical data. Each entry in the two-way table is a frequency.

You can find relative frequencies to interpret the data and describe possible associations between the categories. Relative frequencies are expressed as ratios. They can be written as fractions, decimals, or percents.

Offline Learning: Patterns in Two-Way Tables [offline]

Read pages 262–265 in the reference guide.

Problem Sets

Complete Problems 1–9 odd and 15–25 on pages 266–267.

Lesson Assessment: Patterns in Two-Way Tables Quiz [online]

Go back online to complete the Lesson Quiz.

Student Guide

Scatter Plots

You may have noticed that the more active you are during the day, the more you sleep at night. Or you may have noticed that the more time you spend studying, the higher your test score is. Both situations describe bivariate data, or data that have two variables. In this lesson, you will learn to create scatter plots using bivariate data. You will use the plots to gather information about the data.

Goals for This Lesson
- Create scatter plots from given data.

- Interpret scatter plots.

Graded Activities in This Lesson
Lesson Quiz (computer-scored)

Materials
Intermediate Mathematics C: A Reference Guide and Problem Sets, pages 268–273

Optional

calculator

Keywords
mean (average): the sum of the values in a data set divided by the number of values

median: for a data set with an odd number of values, the middle value after the values have been ordered from least to greatest; for a data set with an even number of values, the mean of the two middle values after the values have been ordered from least to greatest

mode: the data value(s) occurring most often in a data set

quantitative data: data that represent a quantity; numeric data

range: the largest number in a dataset minus the smallest number

scatter plot: a graph that displays two-dimensional data as points; scatter-plot points represent ordered pairs

Learn: Creating Scatter Plots [online]
You will learn how to create scatter plots.

Summarize what you learned in this activity.
1. What is a scatter plot?

2. Describe how you would create a scatter plot from a given set of data.

Worked Examples: Try Creating Scatter Plots [online]

Use the space below to work through the examples you see in the online screens.

Learn: Interpreting Scatter Plots [online]

You will learn how to interpret scatter plots.

Summarize what you learned in this activity.

Describe how to find the following information from a scatter plot:

1. Mean

2. Median

3. Mode

4. Range

Worked Examples: Try Interpreting Scatter Plots [online]

Use the space below to work through the examples you see in the online screens.

Summary: Scatter Plots [online]

To create a scatter plot:
- Number and label the *x*- and *y*-axes using the data. Use the *x*-axis for the independent variable and the *y*-axis for the dependent variable if applicable.
- Plot the points on the graph.

To interpret a scatter plot:
- Determine whether the scatter plot shows a pattern. The data points may follow a line upward or downward or may follow a curve.
- Gather information about the scatter plot. Find the mean, median, mode, or range when asked.

Offline Learning: Scatter Plots [offline]

Read pages 268–271 in the reference guide.

Problem Sets

Complete Problems 1–5 odd and 9–17 odd on pages 271–273.

Lesson Assessment: Scatter Plots Quiz [online]

Go back online to complete the Lesson Quiz.

Student Guide

Clusters and Outliers

A clothing store sells different T-shirts at the following prices:

$15.24, $8.45, $7.98, $8.99, $7.89, $3.00.

You may notice that the prices $15.24 and $3.00 stand out compared to the other prices because they are, respectively, higher or lower. You may also notice that the other prices are clustered closer together. In this lesson, you will learn how to identify both clusters of data points and outlying points (points that lie apart from most of the other points) in data displayed in scatter plots.

Goals for This Lesson
- . Identify clusters and outliers in a scatter plot.

Graded Activities in This Lesson
Lesson Quiz (computer-scored)

Materials
Intermediate Mathematics C: A Reference Guide and Problem Sets, pages 274–277

Keywords
cluster: in a scatter plot, a group of points that are close together in comparison with the other points

outlier: a data value in a data set that is either much smaller or much larger than the other data values in the set

Groundwork: Preparing for the Lesson [online]
You will review how to identify points on a graph.

Learn: Identifying Clusters and Outliers [online]
You will learn to identify clusters and outliers.

Summarize what you learned in this activity.
1. What is a cluster?

2. What is an outlier?

Worked Examples: Try Identifying Clusters and Outliers [online]

Use the space below to work through the examples you see in the online screens.

Summary: Clusters and Outliers [online]

To identify a cluster in a scatter plot:
- Look for data points that are grouped close together.
- Describe the cluster using the range of x- or y-coordinates that show the boundaries of its location.

To identify an outlier in a scatter plot:
- Look for any data points whose values are much larger or much smaller than those of the other data points.
- Describe the outlier using the variables that pinpoint its location.

Offline Learning: Clusters and Outliers [offline]

Read pages 274–275 in the reference guide.

Problem Sets

Complete Problems 2–18 even on pages 276–277.

Lesson Assessment: Clusters and Outliers Quiz [online]

Go back online to complete the Lesson Quiz.

Student Guide

Associations in Scatter Plots

When gathering evidence at a crime scene, investigators carefully look for footprints. A person's shoe size is related to his or her height, so investigators can measure a footprint to estimate a person's height. This information, along with the type of shoe and individual wear marks, is a clue that investigators can use to link a suspect to a crime.

Many variables in our world have a relationship to, or an *association* with, each other. In this lesson, you will learn how to identify and describe associations by using scatter plots.

Goals for This Lesson
- Describe patterns in data.

Graded Activities in This Lesson
Lesson Quiz (computer-scored)

Materials
Intermediate Mathematics C: A Reference Guide and Problem Sets, pages 278–284

Keywords
linear association: in a scatter plot, the points follow a pattern that resembles a line

negative association: an inverse relationship; as the value of one variable goes up, the value of the other variable tends to go down

no association: a lack of association between two variables on a scatter plot

nonlinear association: in a scatter plot, the points follow a pattern that does not resemble a line

positive association: a direct relationship; as the value of one variable goes up, the value of the other variable tends to go up, too

Groundwork: Preparing for the Lesson [online]
You will review determining whether a line has a positive or a negative slope.

Learn: Identifying Associations in Scatter Plots [online]
You will identify positive, negative, linear, nonlinear, and no association in scatter plots.

Summarize what you learned in this activity.

1. What is a positive linear association?

2. What is a negative nonlinear association?

Worked Examples: Try Identifying Associations in Scatter Plots [online]

Use the space below to work through the examples you see in the online screens.

Summary: Associations in Scatter Plots [online]

Scatter plots can have a positive association, a negative association, or no association:

- When data points increase from left to right, there is a positive association.
- When data points decrease from left to right, there is a negative association.
- When data points neither increase nor decrease from left to right, there is no association.

Scatter plots can also follow a linear or a nonlinear association.

Offline Learning: Associations in Scatter Plots [offline]

Read pages 278–282 in the reference guide.

Problem Sets

Complete Problems 1–19 odd on pages 282–284.

Lesson Assessment: Associations in Scatter Plots Quiz [online]

Go back online to complete the Lesson Quiz.

Student Guide

Fitting a Line to Data

Scientists might notice a negative linear pattern in a scatter plot that represents the population of a certain bird species. It would be helpful for them to be able to predict when the bird population will decrease to a certain point or even become extinct. Using a linear model of the data in the scatter plot, they can make such predictions. In this lesson, you will learn to draw an approximate linear model of the data in a scatter plot. You will also find the equation of your model and use that equation to make predictions about the data the line represents.

Goals for This Lesson
- Use a linear model to approximate relationships between two quantitative variables.

Graded Activities in This Lesson
Lesson Quiz (computer-scored)

Materials
Intermediate Mathematics C: A Reference Guide and Problem Sets, pages 285–292

Optional
calculator

Keywords
linear model: a line drawn to fit the trend of the points in a scatter plot

Groundwork: Preparing for the Lesson [online]
You will review writing equations of lines in slope-intercept form.

Learn: Drawing and Using Lines [online]
You will learn to draw a linear model and to find the equation of the line for data in a scatter plot.

Summarize what you learned in this activity.
1. What is a linear model?

2. Describe the steps you can use to find the equation of a linear model.

Worked Examples: Try Drawing and Using Lines [online]

Use the space below to work through the examples you see in the online screens.

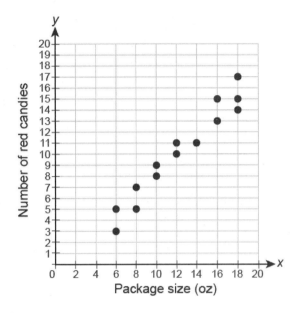

MathCast: Drawing and Using Lines [online]

View the video to see how to solve a typical problem.

Summary: Fitting a Line to Data [online]

You can draw a linear model for data in a scatter plot. Draw the line so that it follows the trend of the data. About half the points should fall above the line and half the points should fall below the line.

To write the equation of the line, identify two points on the line. You can use the equation of the line to make predictions based on the data.

Offline Learning: Fitting a Line to Data [offline]

Read pages 285–289 in the reference guide.

Problem Sets

Complete Problems 2–20 even on pages 290–292.

Lesson Assessment: Fitting a Line to Data Quiz [online]

Go back online to complete the Lesson Quiz.

Student Guide

Core Focus: Interpreting Slopes and Intercepts

When purchasing a new car, a buyer might research the cost of the car based on the features he or she wants. The buyer will discover that the cost of the car starts at a minimum price and increases as features are added. In math, the minimum price in this situation would be called the initial value, and the amount the price increases would be the rate. In this lesson, you'll use linear models to interpret rate and initial value for different situations.

Goals for This Lesson
- Interpret the slope as the rate for a linear model.

- Interpret the *y*-intercept as the initial value for a linear model.

Graded Activities in This Lesson
There is no graded activity associated with this lesson.

Materials
Intermediate Mathematics C: A Reference Guide and Problem Sets, pages 293–295

Keywords and Pronunciation
initial amount: the beginning value of a linear relationship before any time has passed; the initial amount, also known as the initial value, is the *y*-intercept of the line

rate of change: the rate at which quantities change over time in a linear relationship; the rate of change is the slope of the line

Learn: Interpreting Linear Models [online]
Use the space below to take notes during this activity.

Linear Models for Data

Drawing Conclusions from Linear Models

Summary

Offline Learning: Core Focus: Interpreting Slopes and Intercepts [offline]

Read pages 293–294.

Problem Sets

Complete Problems 1–2 on page 295.

Student Guide

Unit Review

You have learned to solve problems involving direct linear variation and quadratic variation, to solve problems involving two-way tables and categorical variables, to create and interpret scatter plots, and to solve problems using linear models. Now it's time to pull together what you have learned.

Goals for This Lesson

- Find the constant of variation when given data for a function with direct linear variation.

- Solve a problem involving direct linear variation.

- Solve problems involving direct variation.

- Find the constant of variation when given data for a function with quadratic variation.

- Solve a problem involving quadratic variation.

- Write a formula for a problem involving a quadratic variation.

- Graph a function involving a quadratic variation.

- Construct and interpret a two-way table summarizing data on two categorical variables collected from the same subjects.

- Use relative frequencies calculated for rows or columns to describe possible associations between bivariate categorical data.

- Create scatter plots from given data.

- Interpret scatter plots.

- Identify clusters and outliers in a scatter plot.

- Describe patterns in data.

- Use a linear model to approximate relationships between two quantitative variables.

- Interpret the slope as the rate for a linear model.

- Interpret the y-intercept as the initial value for a linear model.

Graded Activities in This Lesson

There is no graded activity associated with this lesson.

Materials

Intermediate Mathematics C: A Reference Guide and Problem Sets, pages 296–297

Optional
calculator

Keywords

bivariate data: data that show the relationship between two variables; paired data

categorical variable: a variable that is separable into mutually exclusive groups (for example, boys and girls or athletes and nonathletes)

cluster: in a scatter plot, a group of points that are close together in comparison with the other points

direct variation: a function defined by an equation of the form $y = kx$, where k is a nonzero constant; when you use this equation, you can say that y varies directly as x

frequency: the number of observations within a range of data

initial amount: the beginning value of a linear relationship before any time has passed; the initial amount, also known as the initial value, is the y-intercept of the line

linear model: a line drawn to fit the trend of the points in a scatter plot

linear association: in a scatter plot, the points follow a pattern that resembles a line

mean (average): the sum of the values in a data set divided by the number of values

median: for a data set with an odd number of values, the middle value after the values have been ordered from least to greatest; for a data set with an even number of values, the mean of the two middle values after the values have been ordered from least to greatest

mode: the data value(s) occurring most often in a data set

negative association: an inverse relationship; as the value of one variable goes up, the value of the other variable tends to go down

no association: a lack of association between two variables on a scatter plot

nonlinear association: in a scatter plot, the points follow a pattern that does not resemble a line

outlier: a data value in a data set that is either much smaller or much larger than the other data in the set

positive association: a direct relationship; as the value of one variable goes up, the value of the other variable tends to go up, too

quadratic variation: a relationship between x and y in which you can write the function describing the relationship in a form of the general equation $y = kx^2$, where k is a nonzero constant

range: the largest number in a dataset minus the smallest number

rate of change: the rate at which quantities change over time in a linear relationship; the rate of change is the slope of the line

relative frequency: the number of observations within a given class or category, divided by the total

number of observations: $\dfrac{\#\ of\ observations\ within\ a\ class}{total\ \#\ of\ observations}$; if there is more than one class, each relative frequency will be less than 1, and all relative frequencies will add up to 1

scatter plot: a graph that displays two-dimensional data as points; scatter-plot points represent ordered pairs

two-way table: a table used to compare two categorical variables

Unit Review: Practice Quiz [online]

The last screen of the Practice Quiz will show you how many times you attempted each problem. For each problem, record your number of attempts below. Complete the activities and reference guide problems that correspond with the Practice Quiz problems that took you more than one attempt. Check off the review activities and review problems as you complete them.

Problem 1
Attempts: _____
☐ Complete review activities online.
☐ Complete Problems 9–16 on page 256.

Problem 2
Attempts: _____
□ Complete review activities online.
□ Complete Problems 23–28 on page 256.

Problem 3
Attempts: _____
□ Complete review activities online.
□ Complete Problems 9–16 on page 261.

Problem 4
Attempts: _____
□ Complete review activities online.
□ Complete Problems 1–8 on page 266.

Problem 5
Attempts: _____
□ Complete review activities online.
□ Complete Problems 9–14 on page 266.

Problem 6
Attempts: _____
□ Complete review activities online.
□ Complete Problems 1–10 on pages 271–273.

Problem 7
Attempts: _____
□ Complete review activities online.
□ Complete Problems 1–6 on page 276.

Problem 8
Attempts: _____
□ Complete review activities online.
□ Complete Problems 15–17 on page 284.

Problem 9
Attempts: _____
□ Complete review activities online.
□ Complete Problems 9–20 on pages 291–292.

Problem 10
Attempts: _____
□ Complete review activities online.
□ Complete Problems 1–2 on page 295.

Offline Learning: Linear Models Review [offline]

Complete all the Chapter Review problems on pages 296–297. Use the Topic Lookup at the bottom of page 297 to review topics for any problems that were difficult for you.

Student Guide

Linear Models Test

You have learned to solve problems involving direct linear variation and quadratic variation, to solve problems involving two-way tables and categorical variables, to create and interpret scatter plots, and to solve problems using a linear model. Now it's time to take the Unit Test. This Unit Test has two parts—one part that will be scored by the computer and one part that your Learning Coach will score. You will complete the computer-scored part first.

Goals for This Lesson

- Find the specific equation for a linear variation.

- Find the specific equation for a quadratic variation.

- Graph a function involving a quadratic variation.

- Construct and interpret a two-way table summarizing data on two categorical variables collected from the same subjects.

- Use relative frequencies calculated for rows or columns to describe possible associations between bivariate categorical data.

- Interpret scatter plots.

- Describe patterns in data.

- Use a linear model to approximate relationships between two quantitative variables..

- Interpret the slope as the rate for a linear model.

- Interpret the *y*-intercept as the initial value for a linear model.

- Create scatter plots from given data.

Graded Activities in This Lesson

Linear Models Test, Part 1

Linear Models Test, Part 2

Unit Assessment: Linear Models Test, Part 1 [online]

This part of the Unit Test is online. It will be scored by the computer.

Unit Assessment: Linear Models Test, Part 2 [offline]

This part of the Unit Test is offline.

1. Complete each question on your own. Show all your work.

2. Submit this part to your Learning Coach for a grade.

Student Guide

Extended Problems: Reasoning

In this lesson, you'll complete Extended Problems: Reasoning for the Linear Models unit.

Goals for This Lesson
* Analyze complex problems using mathematical knowledge and skills.

___

Graded Activities in This Lesson
Extended Problems: Reasoning

___

Extended Problems: Reasoning [offline]
You will complete a graded assignment that focuses on reasoning in math.

Your Learning Coach will score this assignment.

* **Complete** the assignment on your own.
* **Submit** the completed assignment to your Learning Coach.

Student Guide

Points, Lines, and Planes

In geometry, you will describe shapes and define their properties. Where do you start? The best place to start is with three basic terms—point, line, and plane. As you will see throughout your study of geometry, these basic terms are the building blocks for many other geometric terms.

Goals for This Lesson
- Name points, lines and planes.
- Identify points, lines, or planes in a figure.

Graded Activities in This Lesson
Lesson Quiz (computer-scored)

Materials
Intermediate Mathematics C: A Reference Guide and Problem Sets, pages 303–307

Keywords
point: a location in space with no length, width, or depth

line: a straight path of points that goes on forever in both directions

plane: a flat surface with infinite length and width but no thickness

Learn: Basic Geometric Figures [online]
You will learn how to name and describe points, lines, and planes.

Summarize what you learned in this activity.

1. What is a point?

2. How are points named?

3. What is a line?

4. Name the line in as many ways as possible.

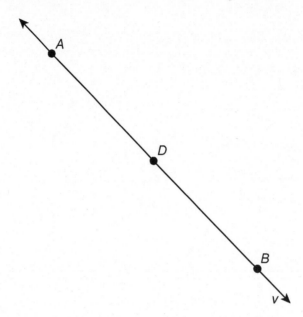

5. What is a plane?

6. Give at least two possible names for the plane.

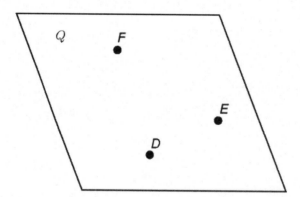

Worked Examples: Try Basic Geometric Figures [online]

Use the space below to work through the examples you see in the online screens.

Summary: Points, Lines, and Planes [online]

Points, lines, and planes are the building blocks for other geometric figures.

- You can name a point with a single capital letter.
- You can name a line by naming two points on the line. You can also name a line with a single lowercase letter.
- You can name a plane by naming three nonlinear points on the plane. You can also name a plane with a single, capital script letter.

Offline Learning: Points, Lines, and Planes [offline]

Read pages 303–305 in the reference guide.

Problem Sets

Complete Problems 1–23 odd on pages 306–307.

Lesson Assessment: Points, Lines, and Planes Quiz [online]

Now go back online to complete the Lesson Quiz.

Student Guide

Pairs of Angles

If you are talking about a house that is *adjacent* to another house, then you are talking about a house that is *next* to it. In the real world, adjacent objects or areas may or may not share a border. In geometry, adjacent angles share a side.

This lesson will teach you about adjacent angles as well as other special pairs of angles.

Goals for This Lesson
- Identify linear pairs, vertical angles, and adjacent angles.
- Find measures of complements and/or supplements of angles.
- Solve problems involving pairs of angles.

Graded Activities in This Lesson
Lesson Quiz (computer-scored)

Materials
Intermediate Mathematics C: A Reference Guide and Problem Sets, pages 308–314

Optional
calculator

Keywords
adjacent angles: two angles in the same plane that share a vertex and a side, but do not share any interior points

complementary angles: a pair of angles for which the sum of their measures is 90°

linear pair: two angles that have a common side and whose other sides point in opposite directions

supplementary angles: a pair of angles for which the sum of their measures is 180°

vertical angles: a pair of nonadjacent angles formed by two intersecting lines

Groundwork: Preparing for the Lesson [online]
You will review lines, rays, and angles. You will also review how to solve equations for a variable.

Learn: Based on Position [online]

You will learn about five types of angles.

Summarize what you learned in this activity.

1. Adjacent angles have a common _____ and a common _____, but they do not have any common _____ points.

2. In a linear pair, the sides that are not common point in _____ directions, forming a _____.

3. Name the linear pairs formed by lines *s* and *t*.

4. Name the vertical angles formed by lines *s* and *t*.

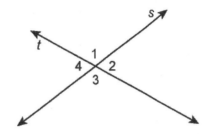

5. Vertical angle pairs are always _____.

Learn: Based on Measure [online]

You will learn how to determine angle measures based on the angle types.

Summarize what you learned in this activity.

1. The measures of complementary angles have a sum of _____.

2. The measures of supplementary angles have a sum of _____.

3. Name the complementary angles in the figure.

4. Name the supplementary angles in the figure.

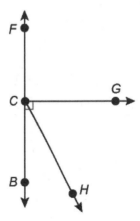

5. If the measure of an angle is *x*, then the measure of its complement is _____.

6. If the measure of an angle is *x*, then the measure of its supplement is _____.

7. ∠A and ∠B are supplementary angles, and the measure of ∠B is 40° less than the measure of ∠A. Find the measure of each angle.

Worked Examples: Pairs of Angles [online]

Use the space below to work through the examples you see in the online screens.

MathCast: Complements [online]

View the video to see how to solve a typical problem

Summary: Pairs of Angles [online]

You learned about five types of angle pairs.

- Adjacent angles are next to each other. They share a vertex and a side but they do not share any interior points.
- Linear pairs are adjacent angles that form a line. Because they form a line, the sum of their measures is 180°.
- Vertical angles are nonadjacent angles formed by 2 intersecting lines. They share a vertex only. Vertical angles are congruent.
- Complementary angles are 2 angles whose measures sum to 90°.
- Supplementary angles are 2 angles whose measures sum to 180°.

Complementary and supplementary angles can be, but do not have to be, adjacent angles.

Offline Learning: Pairs of Angles [offline]

Read pages 308–312 in the reference guide.

Problem Sets

Complete Problems 1–25 odd on pages 313–314.

Lesson Assessment: Pairs of Angles Quiz [online]

Now go back online to complete the Lesson Quiz.

Student Guide

Parallel Lines and Transversals

When you look at a street map, you will see many streets intersecting other streets. You will also see various angles that are formed when the streets intersect. In this lesson, you will learn about the angles formed when a line intersects other lines.

Goals for This Lesson

- Identify a pair of alternate interior and alternate exterior angles associated with a transversal that intersects parallel lines.
- Identify a pair of corresponding angles associated with a transversal that intersects parallel lines.
- Use properties to determine unknown angle measures associated with a transversal that intersects two parallel lines.
- Use properties to determine unknown angle measures associated with a transversal that intersects two parallel lines in a complex figure.

Graded Activities in This Lesson
Lesson Quiz (computer-scored)

Materials
Intermediate Mathematics C: A Reference Guide and Problem Sets, pages 315–319

Optional
calculator

Keywords and Pronunciation
adjacent angles: two angles in the same plane that have a common side and a common vertex, but no common interior points

alternate exterior angles: the outside angles on opposite diagonal sides of a transversal crossing two parallel lines

alternate interior angles: the inside angles on opposite diagonal sides of a transversal crossing two parallel lines

corresponding angles: the angles that lie in the same position or "match up" when a transversal crosses two parallel lines

line: a straight path of points that goes on forever in both directions

parallel lines: coplanar lines that never intersect

transversal: a line that intersects two or more lines in a plane

Groundwork: Preparing for the Lesson [online]
You will review adjacent angles.

Learn: Pairs of Angles Around a Transversal [online]
You will learn about the angles formed when a transversal intersects parallel lines.

Summarize what you learned in this activity.

1. Draw and label 2 parallel lines crossed by a transversal.

2. Number the angles formed, 1–8.

3. Write all the pairs of corresponding angles (there should be four pairs).

4. Write all the pairs of alternate interior angles (there should be two pairs).

5. Write all the pairs of adjacent angles (there should be eight pairs).

Learn: Finding Angle Measures [online]
Summarize what you learned in this activity.

1. Draw 2 parallel lines with a transversal crossing them at 90°. Notice that all 8 angles formed are equal to 90°.

2. Describe the angle relationships by completing the sentences.

    *   Adjacent angles are _____.

    *   Corresponding angles, alternate interior angles, and alternate exterior angles have _____
        _____.

MathCast: Finding Angle Measures [online]
View the video to see how to solve a typical problem.

Summary: Parallel Lines and Transversals [online]
In this lesson, you learned how to identify some of the special angle pairs created when a transversal intersects 2 lines.

You also learned that when the lines are parallel, the corresponding angles, the alternate exterior angles, and the alternate interior angles have equal measures. And you learned that adjacent angles are supplementary.

Offline Learning: Parallel Lines and Transversals [offline]
Read pages 315–317 in the reference guide.

Problem Sets
Complete Problems 1–10 and 11–19 odd on pages 318–319.

Lesson Assessment: Parallel Lines and Transversals Quiz [online]
Now go back online to complete the Lesson Quiz.

Student Guide

Triangles

In newspapers or online, you may have seen classified ads—advertisements that are grouped into various categories, such as Help Wanted, Automobiles, Apartments for Rent, and so forth. To *classify* means to sort or to put into categories. In this lesson, you will learn to classify triangles. When you classify triangles, you will put them into categories according to their angle measures.

Goals for This Lesson
- Classify triangles by angle measures.
- Determine whether a triangle is acute, obtuse, or right.
- Use the triangle sum theorem to find a missing angle measure in a triangle.

Graded Activities in This Lesson
Lesson Quiz (computer-scored)

Materials
Intermediate Mathematics C: A Reference Guide and Problem Sets, pages 320–324

Optional
calculator

Keywords
acute triangle: a triangle with three acute angles

obtuse triangle: a triangle with an obtuse angle

right triangle: a triangle with a right angle

Groundwork: Preparing for the Lesson [online]
You will review how to classify triangles by their sides, as isosceles, scalene, or equilateral. You will also review obtuse, acute, and right angles.

Learn: Classifying Triangles [online]
You will learn how to classify triangles by angle measures.

Summarize what you learned in this activity.

1. In a triangle, each segment is a _____ and each endpoint is a _____.

2.   How do you name a triangle?

3.   Complete the table:

	Definition	Example
Acute triangle		
Right triangle		
Obtuse triangle		

Worked Examples: Try Classifying Triangles [online]

Use the space below to work through the examples you see in the online screens.

Learn: The Triangle Sum Theorem [online]

You will learn the triangle sum theorem.

Summarize what you learned in this activity.

1. The triangle sum theorem states that the measures of the interior angles of a triangle sum to
    _____.

2. Find the value of x.

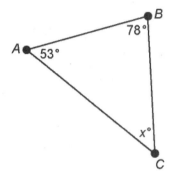

Worked Examples: Find Angle Measures [online]

Use the space below to work through the examples you see in the online screens.

Summary: Triangles [online]

Triangles can be classified by angle measure, as well as side lengths. All triangles have at least 2 acute angles.
- If the third angle is also acute, the triangle is an acute triangle.
- If the third angle is a right angle, the triangle is a right triangle.
- If the third angle is an obtuse angle, the triangle is an obtuse triangle.

The measures of the 3 interior angles of a triangle have a sum of 180°.

Offline Learning: Triangles [offline]

Read pages 320–322 in the reference guide.

Problem Sets

Complete Problems 1–16 on pages 323–324.

Lesson Assessment: Triangles Quiz [online]

Now go back online to complete the Lesson Quiz.

Student Guide

Core Focus: Angles of a Triangle

The triangle sum theorem states that the sum of the measures of the angles of a triangle is 180°. How do you know that this statement is true? In this lesson, you will use what you know about parallel lines, alternate interior angles, and adjacent angles to prove the triangle sum theorem.

Goals for This Lesson
- Identify facts about the angle sum and exterior angles of triangles.

Graded Activities in This Lesson
Lesson Quiz (computer-graded)

Materials
Intermediate Mathematics C: A Reference Guide and Problem Sets, pages 325–327

Optional
calculator

Keywords and Pronunciation
straight angle: an angle that measures 180°

Groundwork: Preparing for the Lesson [online]
You will review how to find a missing angle measure in a triangle.

Summarize what you learned in this activity.
1. What is the sum of the measures of the angles in a triangle?

Learn: Proving the Triangle Sum Theorem [online]
Use the space below to take notes during this activity.

Overview

Proving the Triangle Sum Theorem

Parallel Lines Proof

Copies of a Triangle

Summary

Worked Examples: Proving the Triangle Sum Theorem [online]
Use the space below to work through the examples you see in the online screens.

Offline Learning: Core Focus: Angles of a Triangle [offline]
Read pages 325–326.

Problem Sets
Complete Problems 1–3 on page 327.

Lesson Assessment: Core Focus: Angles of a Triangle Quiz [online]
Go back online to complete the Lesson Quiz.

Student Guide

Polygons

Many street signs are shaped like polygons. A speed limit sign is a convex polygon. Stop signs and yield signs are regular polygons.

After this lesson, you will see polygons everywhere and be able to classify them by different criteria.

Goals for This Lesson
- Classify a polygon by the number of sides and determine if it is concave or convex.
- Determine the sum of the measures of the interior angles of a polygon given the number of sides, and vice versa.
- Identify regular polygons and determine the measure of each interior angle.

Graded Activities in This Lesson
Lesson Quiz (computer-scored)

Materials
Intermediate Mathematics C: A Reference Guide and Problem Sets, pages 328–332

Optional
calculator

Keywords
concave polygon: a polygon in which at least one line segment that connects any two points inside the polygon does not lie completely inside the polygon

convex polygon: a polygon in which every line segment connecting any two points inside the polygon lies completely inside the polygon

diagonal: a segment that connects two vertices of a polygon and does not lie along any side of the polygon

equiangular polygon: a polygon with all angles congruent

equilateral polygon: a polygon with all sides congruent

interior angle: any of the angles inside a polygon

polygon: a closed figure formed by three or more line segments in a plane, such that each line segment intersects exactly two other line segments at their endpoints only

regular polygon: a polygon that is both equilateral and equiangular

side (of a polygon): one of the line segments that form a polygon

vertex (of a polygon): a point where the sides of the polygon intersect; the plural of vertex is vertices

Groundwork: Preparing for the Lesson [online]

You will review the triangle sum theorem.

Learn: Polygon Basics [online]

You will learn how to classify polygons.

Summarize what you learned in this activity.

1. A figure must meet the following requirements to be a polygon.

   • be a _____ figure

   • be a _____ figure

   • be formed by _____ only

   • be formed by segments that intersect exactly _____ other segments

   • be formed by segments that intersect at their _____ only

2. Describe how you can determine whether a polygon is concave or convex.

3. How do you name a polygon?

4. What is an *n*-gon?

Learn: Interior Angle Measures [online]

You will learn how to determine the sum of the interior angle measures of a polygon.

Summarize what you learned in this activity.

1. The formula for the sum of the measures of the interior angles of a polygon is

   _____, where *n* = _____.

2. Find the sum of the measures of the interior angles of a hexagon.

Learn: Regular Polygons [online]

You will learn how to identify a regular polygon.

Summarize what you learned in this activity.

1. What is a regular polygon?

2. Find the measure of each angle in a regular 16-gon.

3. Find the number of sides in a polygon if each interior angle measures 135°.

Worked Examples: Polygons [online]

Use the space below to work through the examples you see in the online screens.

MathCast: How Many Sides? [online]

View the video to see how to solve a typical problem.

Summary: Polygons [online]

Polygons are closed figures formed by 3 or more line segments in a plane, such that each line segment intersects exactly 2 other line segments at their endpoints only.

Polygons are either convex or concave. If a polygon is convex, any segment whose endpoints are inside the polygon will lie completely inside the polygon.

A convex polygon is a regular polygon if all its sides and angles are congruent.

To find the sum of the measures of the interior angles of a convex polygon, multiply 180° by 2 less than the number of sides. This formula works because the number of nonoverlapping triangles that can be formed with the same vertices is 2 less than the number of sides. If a convex polygon is a regular polygon, you can also find the measure of each interior angle.

Offline Learning: Polygons [offline]

Read pages 328–331 in the reference guide.

Problem Sets

Complete Problems 1–29 odd on pages 331–332.

Lesson Assessment: Polygons Quiz [online]

Now go back online to complete the Lesson Quiz.

Student Guide

Core Focus: Exterior Angles

You have learned to find the measures of angles inside a triangle. What if you need to know the measure of an angle outside the triangle? In this lesson, you will learn how to find the measure of an exterior angle.

Goals for This Lesson
* Use properties to determine unknown values associated with internal and external angles of a triangle.

Graded Activities in This Lesson
There is no graded activity associated with this lesson.

Materials
Intermediate Mathematics C: A Reference Guide and Problem Sets, pages 333–335

Optional
calculator

Keywords and Pronunciation
exterior angle of a polygon: an angle formed by two sides of a polygon, one of which extends outside the polygon; each interior angle of a polygon forms a linear pair with an exterior angle

Learn: Exterior Angles [online]
Use the space below to take notes during this activity.

Overview

Exploring Exterior Angles of a Triangle

Summary

Offline Learning: Core Focus: Exterior Angles [offline]
Read pages 333–334.

Problem Sets
Complete Problems 1–6 on page 335.

Student Guide

Unit Review

You have learned to classify basic geometric shapes, such as points, lines, angles, and polygons; to find measures of angles and line segments in triangles and polygons; and to verify properties of different geometric shapes. Now it's time to pull together what you have learned.

Goals for This Lesson

- Identify points, lines, or planes in a figure.

- Name points, lines, and planes.

- Identify a pair of alternate interior and alternate exterior angles associated with a transversal that intersects parallel lines.

- Identify a pair of corresponding angles associated with a transversal that intersects parallel lines.

- Use properties to determine unknown angle measures associated with a transversal that intersects two parallel lines.

- Use properties to determine unknown angle measures associated with a transversal that intersects two parallel lines in a complex figure.

- Identify linear pairs, vertical angles, and adjacent angles.

- Solve problems involving pairs of angles.

- Find measures of complements and/or supplements of angles.

- Classify triangles by angle measures.

- Use the triangle sum theorem to find a missing angle measure in a triangle.

- Determine whether a triangle is acute, obtuse, or right.

- Use triangle properties to find missing angle measures in a triangle.

- Identify facts about the angle sum and exterior angles of triangles.

- Classify a polygon by the number of sides and determine if it is concave or convex.

- Determine the sum of the measures of the interior angles of a polygon given the number of sides, and vice versa.

- Identify regular polygons and determine the measure of each interior angle.

- Use properties to determine unknown values associated with internal and external angles of a triangle.

Graded Activities in This Lesson
There is no graded activity associated with this lesson.

Materials
Intermediate Mathematics C: A Reference Guide and Problem Sets, pages 336–337

Optional
calculator

Keywords

acute angle: an angle that measures less than 90°

acute triangle: a triangle with three acute angles

adjacent angles: two angles in the same plane that share a vertex and a side, but do not share any interior points

alternate exterior angles: the outside angles on opposite diagonal sides of a transversal crossing two parallel lines

alternate interior angles: the inside angles on opposite diagonal sides of a transversal crossing two parallel lines

angle: the figure formed by two rays, called sides, that share the same endpoint

complementary angles: a pair of angles for which the sum of their measures is 90°

concave polygon: a polygon in which at least one line segment that connects any two points inside the polygon does not lie completely inside the polygon

congruent angles: angles that have equal measures

congruent segments: segments that have equal lengths

convex polygon: a polygon in which every line segment connecting any two points inside the polygon lies completely inside the polygon

corresponding angles: the angles that lie in the same position or "match up" when a transversal crosses two parallel lines

diagonal: a segment that connects two vertices of a polygon and does not lie along any side of the polygon

exterior angle of a polygon: an angle formed by two sides of a polygon, one of which extends outside the polygon; each interior angle of a polygon forms a linear pair with an exterior angle

interior angle: any of the angles inside a polygon

length (of a line segment): the distance between its endpoints

line: a collection of points arranged in a straight path

line segment: part of a line that includes any two points on the line and all the points in between the two points

linear pair: two angles that have a common side and whose other sides point in opposite directions

obtuse angle: an angle that measures greater than 90° and less than 180°

obtuse triangle: a triangle with an obtuse angle

parallel lines: coplanar lines that never intersect

polygon: a closed figure formed by three or more line segments in a plane, such that each line segment intersects exactly at two other line segments at their endpoints only

regular polygon: a polygon that is both equilateral and equiangular

right angle: an angle that measures 90°

right triangle: a triangle with a right angle

side (of a polygon): one of the line segments that form a polygon

straight angle: an angle that measures 180°

supplementary angles: a pair of angles for which the sum of their measures is 180°

transversal: a line that intersects two or more lines in a plane

vertex: a point common to two sides of an angle or polygon; the plural of vertex is vertices

vertical angles: a pair of nonadjacent angles formed by two intersecting lines

Unit Review: Practice Quiz [online]

The last screen of the Practice Quiz will show you how many times you attempted each problem. For each problem, record your number of attempts below. Complete the activities and reference guide problems that correspond with the Practice Quiz problems that took you more than one attempt. Check off the review activities and review problems as you complete them.

Problem 1
Attempts: _____
□ Complete review activities online.
□ Complete Problems 1–14 on page 306.

Problem 2
Attempts: _____
□ Complete review activities online.
□ Complete Problems 1–10 on page 318

Problem 3
Attempts: _____
□ Complete review activities online.
□ Complete Problems 1–10 on page 318.

Problem 4
Attempts: _____
□ Complete review activities online.
□ Complete Problems 11–13 on page 318.

Problem 5
Attempts: _____
□ Complete review activities online.
□ Complete Problems 14–17 on page 318.

Problem 6
Attempts: _____
□ Complete review activities online.
□ Complete Problems 1–8 on pages 313–314.

Problem 7
Attempts: _____
□ Complete review activities online.
□ Complete Problems 1–6 on page 323.

Problem 8
Attempts: _____
□ Complete review activities online.
□ Complete Problems 7–16 on pages 323–324.

Problem 9

Attempts: _____
□ Complete review activities online.
□ Complete Problems 25–30 on page 332.

Problem 10

Attempts: _____
□ Complete review activities online.
□ Complete Problems 1–5 on page 335.

Offline Learning: Basic Geometric Shapes Review [online]

Complete all the Chapter Review problems on pages 336–337. Use the Topic Lookup at the bottom of page 337 to review topics for any problems that were difficult for you.

Student Guide

Basic Geometric Shapes Test

You have learned to classify basic geometric shapes, such as points, lines, angles, and polygons; to find measures of angles and line segments in triangles and polygons; and to verify properties of different geometric shapes. Now it's time to take the Unit Test. This Unit Test has two parts—one part that will be scored by the computer and one part that your Learning Coach will score. You will complete the computer-scored part first.

Goals for This Lesson

- Identify points, lines, or planes in a figure.

- Name points, lines, and planes.

- Identify a pair of alternate interior and alternate exterior angles associated with a transversal that intersects parallel lines.

- Identify a pair of corresponding angles associated with a transversal that intersects parallel lines.

- Use properties to determine unknown angle measures associated with a transversal that intersects two parallel lines.

- Use properties to determine unknown angle measures associated with a transversal that intersects two parallel lines in a complex figure.

- Identify linear pairs, vertical angles, and adjacent angles.

- Solve problems involving pairs of angles.

- Find measures of complements and/or supplements of angles.

- Use the triangle sum theorem to find a missing angle measure in a triangle.

- Determine whether a triangle is acute, obtuse, or right.

- Classify a polygon by the number of sides and determine if it is concave or convex.

- Determine the sum of the measures of the interior angles of a polygon given the number of sides, and vice versa.

- Identify regular polygons and determine the measure of each interior angle.

- Use properties to determine unknown values associated with internal and external angles of a triangle.

Graded Activities in This Lesson

Basic Geometric Shapes Test, Part 1

Basic Geometric Shapes Test, Part 2

Unit Test: Basic Geometric Shapes Test, Part 1 [online]

This part of the Unit Test is online. It will be scored by the computer.

Unit Test: Basic Geometric Shapes Test, Part 2 [offline]

This part of the Unit Test is offline.

1. Complete each question on your own. Show all your work.

---

2. Submit this part to your Learning Coach for a grade.

Student Guide

Extended Problems: Reasoning

In this lesson, you'll complete Extended Problems: Reasoning for the Basic Geometric Shapes unit.

Goals for This Lesson
- Analyze complex problems using mathematical knowledge and skills.

Graded Activities in This Lesson
Extended Problems: Reasoning

Extended Problems: Reasoning [offline]
You will complete a graded assignment that focuses on reasoning in math.

Your Learning Coach will score this assignment.

- **Complete** the assignment on your own.
- **Submit** the completed assignment to your Learning Coach.

Student Guide

Volumes of Cylinders

Cylinders are like prisms because both have 2 bases that are parallel. The main difference between a prism and a cylinder is that the bases of a prism are always polygons, and the bases of a cylinder are circles. In this lesson, you will learn more about cylinders and how to find the volume of a cylinder.

Goals for This Lesson
- Find the exact volume of a cylinder.

- Use an approximation for pi to estimate the volume of a cylinder.

Graded Activities in This Lesson
Lesson Quiz (computer-scored)

Materials
Intermediate Mathematics C: A Reference Guide and Problem Sets, pages 343–345

Optional
calculator

Keywords and Pronunciation
base of a cylinder: one of the parallel, congruent faces of the cylinder; a base of a cylinder is a circle

cylinder: a three-dimensional figure with two congruent, parallel bases that are circles and a curved lateral surface that joins them

lateral surface: the curved surface of a cylinder or cone; in a prism, any surface that connects the two bases; in a pyramid, any surface that rises from the base to the vertex

volume: the measure of the space inside (or the space occupied by) a three-dimensional figure

Groundwork: Preparing for the Lesson [online]

You will review volumes of prisms and areas of circles.

Learn: Finding the Volume of a Cylinder [online]

You will learn how to find the volume of a cylinder.

Summarize what you learned in this activity.

1. Describe cylinders in your own words.

2. Explain how to find the volume of a cylinder.

Worked Examples: Try Finding the Volume of a Cylinder [online]

Use the space below to work through the examples you see in the online screens.

MathCast: Volume of a Cylinder [online]

View the video to see how to solve a typical problem.

Summary: Volumes of Cylinders [online]

A general formula for the volume of a cylinder is V = base area • height. Since the bases of a cylinder are circles, the base area is found by using the formula for the area of a circle.

Remember, volume is always expressed in cubic units, such as cm^3 or ft^3.

Offline Learning: Volumes of Cylinders [offline]

Read pages 343–344 in the reference guide.

Problem Sets

Complete Problems 1–15 odd on page 345.

Lesson Assessment: Volumes of Cylinders Quiz [online]

Now go back online to complete the Lesson Quiz.

Student Guide

Applications of Cylinders

When you picture a silo on a farm, what image comes to your mind? Chances are your image includes a cylinder with a rounded top. Farmers need to understand the volume of the cylindrical part in order to figure out the amount of grain they have stored in their silo.

You can find many cylinders in your everyday life. In this lesson, you will learn to apply the formula for finding the volume of a cylinder to real-world problems.

Goals for This Lesson
- Solve problems involving the volume of a cylinder.

Graded Activities in This Lesson
Lesson Quiz (computer-scored)

Materials
Intermediate Mathematics C: A Reference Guide and Problem Sets, pages 346–349

Optional

calculator

Learn: Problems Involving Volumes of Cylinders [online]
Walk through application problems that involve volumes of cylinders.

Summarize what you learned in this activity.
1. List examples of real-world objects that often have a cylindrical shape.

2. A paper towel roll typically has a cardboard tube in the center. Explain how to find the volume of paper towels, given the height of the roll, the radius of the roll, and the radius of the cardboard tube.

Worked Examples: Try Problems Involving Volumes of Cylinders [online]
Use the space below to work through the examples you see in the online screens.

Summary: Applications of Cylinders [online]

You can find many objects in your everyday life that are cylindrical. To determine the volume of any cylinder, apply the formula

$$V = \pi r^2 h.$$

Remember to develop a problem-solving strategy when solving more complex problems.

Offline Learning: Applications of Cylinders [offline]

Read pages 346–348 in the reference guide.

Problem Sets

Complete Problems 1–8 on pages 348–349.

Lesson Assessment: Applications of Cylinders Quiz [online]

Go back online to complete the Lesson Quiz.

Student Guide

Volumes of Cones

Have you ever noticed that a substance like dirt or sand forms a cone-shaped pile when you pour it on a flat surface? You can find the volume of the cone-shaped pile of dirt if you know the dimensions of the cone. In this lesson, you will learn how to find the volume of a cone.

Goals for This Lesson
- Find the volume of a cone using pi or an approximation for pi.

Graded Activities in This Lesson
Lesson Quiz (computer-scored)

Materials
Intermediate Mathematics C: A Reference Guide and Problem Sets, pages 350–353

Optional

calculator

Keywords
cone: a three-dimensional figure with one base that is a circle, a curved lateral surface, and a point called a vertex

vertex of a cone: the point at which the curved surface of cone comes together

Groundwork: Preparing for the Lesson [online]
You will review how to find the volume of a pyramid.

Learn: Defining Cones [online]
You will learn the definition of a cone.

Summarize what you learned in this activity.

1. How is a cone like a pyramid? How is it different from a pyramid?

2. How is a cone like a cylinder? How is it different from a cylinder?

Learn: Finding the Volume of a Cone [online]
You will learn how to find the volume of a cone.

Summarize what you learned in this activity.

1. Write the formula for finding the volume of a cone.

2. Find the volume:
   - A cone that has a height of 14 cm and a base with a radius of 9 cm.

   - A cone-shaped pile of sand that has a height of 4 in. and a base with a diameter of 6 in.

Worked Examples: Try Finding the Volume of a Cone [online]
Use the space below to work through the examples you see in the online screens.

MathCast: Volume of a Cone [online]
View the video to see how to solve a typical problem.

Summary: Volumes of Cones [online]
A cone is a solid with one circular base and a curved lateral surface that converges at a vertex. The height of a cone is the perpendicular distance from the vertex to the base.

The volume of a cone is one-third the volume of a cylinder with the same base area and height.

Offline Learning: Volumes of Cones [offline]
Read pages 350–352 in the reference guide.

Problem Sets
Complete Problems 1–15 odd on pages 352–353.

Lesson Assessment: Volumes of Cones Quiz [online]
Go back online to complete the Lesson Quiz.

Student Guide

Applications of Cones

Where have you seen cones in your everyday life? You have probably seen, and enjoyed, an ice cream cone. You may also have seen traffic cones in a parking lot, or cone-shaped disposable cups in a dispenser. Some older homes and castles have turrets with cone-shaped roofs. In this lesson, you will learn to apply the formula for finding the volume of a cone to real-world problems.

Goals for This Lesson
- Solve problems involving the volume of a cone.

- Solve problems involving volume of solid figures.

Graded Activities in This Lesson
Lesson Quiz (computer-scored)

Materials
Intermediate Mathematics C: A Reference Guide and Problem Sets, pages 354–356

Optional
calculator

Learn: Problems Involving Volumes of Cones [online]
You will apply volume formulas to solve real-world problems involving cones.

Summarize what you learned in this activity.

1. List some examples of cones in your everyday life. How can you find the volume of these cones?

2. If a cone and a cylinder have the same base radius and height, what is the relationship between the volumes?

Worked Examples: Try Problems Involving Volumes of Cones [online]

Use the space below to work through the examples you see in the online screens.

Summary: Applications of Cones [online]

Many objects in the real world are shaped like cones. To determine the volume of any cone, apply the formula

$$V = \frac{1}{3}\pi r^2 h .$$

Remember to develop a problem-solving strategy when solving more complex problems.

Offline Learning: Applications of Cones [offline]

Read pages 354–355 in the reference guide.

Problem Sets

Complete Problems 1–8 on page 356.

Lesson Assessment: Applications of Cones Quiz [online]

Go back online to complete the Lesson Quiz.

Student Guide

Volumes of Spheres

A basketball is a three-dimensional shape called a sphere. To play a game of basketball, the ball must be properly inflated. You can calculate the volume of air inside an inflated basketball if you know its radius and the formula for finding the volume of a sphere. In this lesson, you will learn the formula and how to find exact and approximate volumes of spheres.

Goals for This Lesson
- Find the exact volume of a sphere.
- Find the approximate volume of a sphere.

Graded Activities in This Lesson
Lesson Quiz (computer-scored)

Materials
Intermediate Mathematics C: A Reference Guide and Problem Sets, pages 357–359

Optional
calculator

Keywords
center of a sphere: the point to which all points on the surface of a sphere are equidistant

radius of a sphere: the distance from the center of a sphere to the sphere's surface

sphere: a figure in space made up of all points equidistant from a given point

Groundwork: Preparing for the Lesson [online]
You will review how to find exact and approximate volumes of cylinders.

Learn: Finding the Volume of a Sphere [online]
You will learn how to find the volume of a sphere.

Summarize what you learned in this activity.
1. Define the following in your own words

   - center of a sphere

   - radius of a sphere.

2. Write the formula for the volume of a sphere.

3. How do you write an exact volume for a sphere? What can you do if you only need an approximate volume?

Worked Examples: Try Finding the Volume of a Sphere [online]

Use the space below to work through the examples you see in the online screens.

Summary: Volumes of Spheres [online]

A sphere is a solid in space made up of all points equidistant from a given point.

To find the volume of a sphere, use the formula

$$V = \frac{4}{3}\pi r^3,$$

where r is the radius of the sphere.

Use π for exact volume.

Use 3.14 for approximate volume.

Offline Learning: Volumes of Spheres [offline]

Read pages 357–358 in the reference guide.

Problem Sets

Complete Problems 2–20 even on pages 358–359.

Lesson Assessment: Volumes of Spheres Quiz [online]

Go back online to complete the Lesson Quiz.

Student Guide

Applications of Spheres

A regulation baseball is spherical in shape. It weighs between 5 and 5.24 oz, and has a diameter of 2.875–3 in. Although a baseball looks simple, it is a precision-made object consisting of several layers of different types of materials. Baseball manufacturers need to carefully calculate the amount of material that will fill the volume of the spherical baseball in order to meet the size and weight specifications.

In this lesson, you will apply the formula for the volume of a sphere to solve real-world problems that involve spherical objects.

Goals for This Lesson
- Solve problems involving the exact or approximate volume of a sphere.

- Solve problems involving volume of solid figures.

Graded Activities in This Lesson
Lesson Quiz (computer-scored)

Materials
Intermediate Mathematics C: A Reference Guide and Problem Sets, pages 360–362

Optional
calculator

Learn: Problems Involving Volumes of Spheres [online]
You will use the formula for the volume of a sphere to solve real-world problems.

Summarize what you learned in this activity.
1. Describe some objects in the real world that are spherical.

2. Describe how you can find the volume of the different layers (cork, rubber, and yarn) in a baseball.

3. Describe how you can calculate the number of spherical objects that will fit in a cylindrical container.

Worked Examples: Try Problems Involving Volumes of Spheres [online]

Use the space below to work through the examples you see in the online screens.

Summary: Applications of Spheres [online]

To solve real-world problems involving spherical objects, apply the formula for the volume of a sphere,

$$V_{\text{sphere}} = \frac{4}{3}\pi r^3,$$

where r is the radius of sphere.

Remember to read the problem carefully and to use your problem-solving skills to find the solution.

Offline Learning: Applications of Spheres [offline]

Read pages 360–361 in the reference guide.

Problem Sets

Complete Problems 1–8 on pages 361–362.

Lesson Assessment: Applications of Spheres Quiz [online]

Go back online to complete the Lesson Quiz.

Student Guide

Core Focus: Comparing Volumes

An ice cream store sells ice cream in cones and cups for the same price. The cone and the cup are both filled completely with ice cream, and then a scoop is placed on top. You want to get the most ice cream for your money. How do you know if a cup or a cone holds more ice cream? You can compare the volume of each shape to find your answer. In this lesson, you will learn to compare volumes to solve problems.

Goals for This Lesson
- Solve problems involving the volume of solid figures.

Graded Activities in This Lesson
There is no graded activity associated with this lesson.

Materials
Intermediate Mathematics C: A Reference Guide and Problem Sets, pages 363–365

Optional
calculator

Learn: Comparing Volumes [online]
Use the space below to take notes during this activity.

Overview

Comparing Volumes to Solve Problems

Summary

Offline Learning: Core Focus: Comparing Volumes [offline]
Read pages 363–364.

Problem Sets
Complete Problems 1–4 on page 365.

339

Student Guide

Unit Review

You have learned to find the exact and approximate volumes of cones, cylinders, and spheres. You've also learned to apply the formulas for finding volume to solve real-world problems. Now it's time to pull together what you have learned.

Goals for This Lesson
- Find the exact volume of a cylinder.

- Use an approximation for pi to estimate the volume of a cylinder.

- Solve problems involving the volume of a cylinder.

- Find the volume of a cone using pi or an approximation for pi.

- Solve problems involving the volume of a cone.

- Find the exact volume of a sphere.

- Find the approximate volume of a sphere.

- Solve problems involving the exact or approximate volume of a sphere.

- Solve problems involving volume of solid figures.

Graded Activities in This Lesson
There is no graded activity associated with this lesson.

Materials
Intermediate Mathematics C: A Reference Guide and Problem Sets, pages 366–367

Optional

calculator

Keywords
base of a cylinder: one of the parallel, congruent faces of the cylinder; a base of a cylinder is a circle

center of a sphere: the point to which all points on the surface of a sphere are equidistant

cone: a three-dimensional figure with one base that is a circle, a curved lateral surface, and a point called a vertex

cylinder: a three-dimensional figure with two congruent, parallel bases that are circles and a curved lateral surface that joins them

lateral face: a face that is not a base

lateral surface: the curved surface of a cylinder or cone; in a prism, any surface that connects the two bases; in a pyramid, any surface that rises from the base to the vertex

radius of a sphere: the distance from the center of a sphere to the sphere's surface

sphere: a figure in space made up of all points equidistant from a given point

vertex: a point common to two sides of an angle or polygon; the plural of vertex is vertices

volume: the measure of the space inside (or the space occupied by) a three-dimensional figure

Unit Review: Practice Quiz [online]

The last screen of the Practice Quiz will show you how many times you attempted each problem. For each problem, record your number of attempts below. Complete the activities and reference guide problems that correspond with the Practice Quiz problems that took you more than one attempt. Check off the review activities and review problems as you complete them.

Problem 1
Attempts: _____
□ Complete review activities online.
□ Complete Problems 1–6 and 9–15 on page 345.

Problem 2
Attempts: _____
□ Complete review activities online.
□ Complete Problems 1–6 and 9–15 on page 345.

Problem 3
Attempts: _____
□ Complete review activities online.
□ Complete Problems 1–5 and 7–10 on pages 352–353.

Problem 4
Attempts: _____
□ Complete review activities online.
□ Complete Problems 1–5 and 7–10 on pages 352–353.

Problem 5
Attempts: _____
□ Complete review activities online.
□ Complete Problems 1–16 on pages 358–359.

Problem 6
Attempts: _____
□ Complete review activities online.
□ Complete Problems 1–16 on pages 358–359.

Problem 7
Attempts: _____
□ Complete review activities online.
□ Complete Problems 1–8 on pages 348–349.

Problem 8
Attempts: _____
□ Complete review activities online.
□ Complete Problems 1–8 on page 356

Problem 9
Attempts: _____
□ Complete review activities online.
□ Complete Problems 1–8 on pages 361–362.

Problem 10
Attempts: _____
□ Complete review activities online.
□ Complete Problems 1–4 on page 365.

Offline Learning: Volume Review [offline]

Complete all the Chapter Review problems on pages 366–367. Use the Topic Lookup at the bottom of page 367 to review topics for any problems that were difficult for you.

Student Guide

Volume Test

You have learned to find the exact and approximate volumes of cones, cylinders, and spheres and students have learned to apply the formulas for finding volume to solve real-world problems. Now it's time to take the Unit Test. This Unit Test has two parts—one part that will be scored by the computer and one part that your Learning Coach will score. You will complete the computer-scored part first.

Goals for This Lesson

- Find the exact volume of a cylinder.

- Use an approximation for pi to estimate the volume of a cylinder.

- Find the approximate volume of a cylinder.

- Solve problems involving the volume of a cylinder.

- Find the volume of a cone using pi or an approximation for pi.

- Find the exact volume of a cone.

- Find the approximate volume of a cone.

- Solve problems involving the volume of a cone.

- Find the exact volume of a sphere.

- Find the approximate volume of a sphere.

- Solve problems involving the volume of a sphere.

- Solve problems involving the volumes of cones, cylinders, and spheres.

Graded Activities in This Lesson

Volume Test, Part 1

Volume Test, Part 2

Unit Test:Volume Test, Part 1 [online]

This part of the Unit Test is online. It will be scored by the computer.

Unit Test: Volume Test, Part 2 [offline]

This part of the Unit Test is offline.

1. Complete each question on your own. Show all your work.

2. Submit this part to your Learning Coach for a grade.

Student Guide

Extended Problems: Real-World Application

In this lesson, you'll complete Extended Problems: Real-World Application for the Volume unit.

Goals for This Lesson
- Apply mathematical knowledge and skills to evaluate and analyze real-world situations.

Graded Activities in This Lesson
Extended Problems: Real-World Application

Extended Problems: Real-World Application [offline]
You will complete a graded assignment that focuses on a real-world application of math.

Your teacher will grade this assignment.

- **Save** the graded assignment to your computer. In the filename, replace "studentname" with your last name followed by your first initial.
- **Complete** the assignment on your own.
- **Submit** the completed assignment according to your teacher's instructions.

Student Guide

Congruence and Similarity

When you use a cookie cutter to make cookies, each cookie comes out having the same size and shape. Some polygons look like they were made with a cookie cutter. Others have the same shape but not the same size.

Goals for This Lesson

* Identify congruent and similar polygons.

* Use congruence to find missing side or angle measures.

* Use proportions to find missing side lengths for similar figures.

Graded Activities in This Lesson

Lesson Quiz (computer-scored)

Materials

Intermediate Mathematics C: A Reference Guide and Problem Sets, pages 373–380

Optional

calculator

Keywords

congruent polygons: polygons that are the same size and shape

similar polygons: polygons that have the same shape but not necessarily the same size

Groundwork: Preparing for the Lesson [online]

You will review how to solve proportions.

Learn: Congruent Polygons [online]

You will learn the definition and properties of congruent polygons. You will also learn how to find missing angle measures and side lengths in congruent polygons.

Summarize what you learned in this activity.

1. Congruent polygons have the same _____.

2. The parts that match up are _____ parts.

3. A _____ shows how 2 congruent polygons match up.

4. When you write a congruence statement, write the _____ in the same order.

5. When two polygons are congruent—

• All pairs of corresponding angles are _____.

• All pairs of corresponding sides are _____.

Learn: Similar Polygons [online]

You will learn the definition and properties of similar polygons. You will also learn how to find missing angles and side lengths in similar polygons.

Summarize what you learned in this activity.

1. Similar polygons have the same _____, but not necessarily the same _____.

2. When 2 polygons are similar—

• All pairs of corresponding angles are _____.

• All pairs of corresponding sides are _____.

Worked Examples: Congruence and Similarity [online]

Use the space below to work through the examples you see in the online screens.

Summary: Congruence and Similarity [online]

Congruent polygons are the same size and shape. The corresponding, or matching, angles are congruent, and the corresponding sides are congruent. You can identify corresponding parts from a congruence statement.

Similar polygons are the same shape. The sizes can be different, but the side lengths must be proportional. Because the shapes are the same, the corresponding angles are congruent. You can identify corresponding parts from a similarity statement.

Offline Learning: Congruence and Similarity [offline]

Read pages 373–377 in the reference guide.

Problem Sets

Complete Problems 1–27 odd on pages 378–380.

Lesson Assessment: Congruence and Similarity Quiz [online]

Now go back online to complete the Lesson Quiz.

Student Guide

Similarity and Scale

Think about how you would measure the height of a tall building. It would probably be too difficult using a ruler or some other measuring device. This kind of measurement can be made by using what are called similar figures. In this lesson, you will learn about similar figures and how to make use of their properties.

Goals for the Lesson

- Determine whether two figures are similar and find a missing length in a pair of similar figures.

- Find the scale factor for a pair of similar figures with at least one known pair of corresponding side lengths.

Graded Activities in This Lesson
Lesson Quiz (computer-scored)

Materials
Intermediate Mathematics C: A Reference Guide and Problem Sets, pages 381–385

Optional
calculator

Keywords and Pronunciation
congruent angles: angles that have the same measure

scale factor: a ratio of one measure to another, where both measures are the same unit of measure

similar figures: figures that have the same shape but not necessarily the same size

---

Learn: Identifying Similar Figures [online]
You will learn how to identify similar figures by comparing corresponding angles and corresponding sides. You will also use the proportional sides of similar triangles to find missing side lengths.

Summarize what you learned in this activity.

1. What two things are true about similar figures?

2. Explain how to use the properties of similar figures to find the length of a missing side

---

Learn: Scale Factors [online]

You will learn how to determine scale factors by using the proportions in similar figures.

Summarize what you learned in this activity.

1. Explain how you know whether a figure is a reduction or an enlargement of the original figure.

Worked Examples: Using Scale Factors [online]

Use the space below to work through the examples you see in the online screens.

Summary: Similarity and Scale [online]

Two figures are similar if all the corresponding angles in the two figures are congruent and all the corresponding sides are proportional.

You can use properties of similar figures to find the length of a missing side.

A scale factor is a ratio of one measure to another. You can find the scale factor of a figure by writing the ratio of its corresponding sides.

Offline Learning: Similarity and Scale [offline]

Read pages 381–384 in the reference guide.

Problem Sets

Complete Problems 2–12 even on pages 384–385.

Lesson Assessment: Similarity and Scale Quiz [online]

Now go back online to complete the Lesson Quiz.

Student Guide

Transformations

If you pick up an apple, you can flip it over, turn it around, or move it somewhere else—and you still have the same apple you started with. Mathematically, these kinds of motions are called transformations. In this lesson, you will learn about three kinds of transformations—reflections, rotations, and translations.

Goals for This Lesson
- Determine whether a transformation is a reflection, a rotation, or a translation.

Graded Activities in This Lesson
Lesson Quiz (computer-scored)

Materials
Intermediate Mathematics C: A Reference Guide and Problem Sets, pages 386–392

Optional
calculator

Keywords
center of rotation: the point about which a figure is rotated

image: in a transformation, the new figure that results from the transformation

line of reflection: the line that a figure is reflected across

pre-image: the original figure in a transformation

reflection: a transformation of a figure by flipping it across a line or line segment, creating a mirror image of the figure

rotation: a transformation of a figure by turning it about a given point

transformation: a movement or change of a figure, such as a translation, reflection, rotation, or dilation

translation: the movement of a figure along a line; sometimes called a slide

vector: a line segment with a direction indicated with an arrow

Learn: Translations [online]
You will learn to identify and describe translations.

Summarize what you learned in this activity.

What is a translation?

Learn: Reflections [online]

You will learn to identify and describe reflections.

Summarize what you learned in this activity.

What is a reflection?

Learn: Rotations [online]

You will learn to identify and describe rotations.

Summarize what you learned in this activity.

What is a rotation?

Worked Examples: Try Transformations [online]

Use the space below to work through the examples you see in the online screens.

Summary: Transformations [online]

A transformation is called—

- a *reflection* when a figure is reflected, or flipped, over a line.
- a *rotation* when a figure is rotated, or turned, about a point.
- a *translation* when a figure is translated, or slid, from one location to another.

The figure before a transformation happens is called the *pre-image*. After the transformation, it is called the *image*.

Offline Learning: Transformations [offline]

Read pages 386–390 in the reference guide.

Problem Sets

Complete Problems 1–27 odd on pages 390–392.

Lesson Assessment: Transformations Quiz [online]

Go back online to complete the Lesson Quiz.

Student Guide

Core Focus: Properties of Transformations

Suppose you and your family are moving to a new home. The triangular pennant for your favorite sports team is packed with your belongings. When you get to the new home, you unpack the pennant. As expected, neither the shape nor the size of the pennant was changed during the move. In math, when figures are moved, or transformed, they also maintain the same shape and size. In this lesson, you will use properties of transformation to verify that transformed images have the same shape and size as the original.

Goals for This Lesson
- Experimentally verify the properties of rotations, reflections, and translations.

Graded Activities in This Lesson
Lesson Quiz (computer-graded)

Materials
Intermediate Mathematics C: A Reference Guide and Problem Sets, pages 393–396

Optional
calculator

Groundwork: Preparing for the Lesson [online]
You will review identifying translations, reflections, and rotations.

Learn: Rigid Transformations [online]
Use the space below to take notes during this activity.

Rigid Transformations: Types and Properties

Using Rigid Transformations

Summary

Worked Examples: Try Rigid Transformations [online]

Use the space below to work through the examples you see in the online screens.

Offline Learning: Core Focus: Properties of Transformations

[offline]
Read pages 393–395.

Problem Sets
Complete Problems 1–4 on pages 395–396.

Lesson Assessment: Core Focus: Properties of Transformations Quiz [online]
Go back online to complete the Lesson Quiz.

Student Guide

Sequences of Transformations

Rigid transformations, such as translations, reflections, and rotations, result in congruent figures. In this lesson, you will investigate sequences of transformations, such as a reflection followed by a rotation. You will learn how sequences of transformations affect figures.

Goals for This Lesson
- Describe a transformation using a sequence of transformations.

Graded Activities in This Lesson
Lesson Quiz (computer-scored)

Materials
Intermediate Mathematics C: A Reference Guide and Problem Sets, pages 397–399

Optional
calculator

Keywords
dilation: a transformation that changes the size, but not the shape, of a figure

similar figures: figures that are the same shape but not necessarily the same size; congruent figures are also similar

Learn: Rotations, Reflections, and Translations [online]
You will describe sequences of transformations.

Summarize what you learned in this activity.
1. What type of figures do reflections, rotations, and translations produce?

2. In a sequence of transformations, explain how you know that the pre-image is congruent to the final image.

Worked Examples: Try Rotations, Reflections, and Translations [online]

Use the space below to work through the examples you see in the online screens.

Summary: Sequences of Transformations [online]

Reflections, rotations, and translations are rigid transformations, which produce congruent figures. If a figure goes through a sequence of reflections, rotations, and/or translations, the pre-image will be congruent to all images formed in the sequence.

Offline Learning: Sequences of Transformations [offline]

Read pages 397–398 in the reference guide.

Problem Sets

Complete Problems 1–6 on page 399.

Lesson Assessment: Sequences of Transformations Quiz [online]

Go back online to complete the Lesson Quiz.

Student Guide

Transformations and Coordinates

Reflections, rotations, and translations result in images that are congruent to the pre-image. The sizes of the figures don't change, only the position. What if those transformations were done on the coordinate plane? How would the coordinates be affected? In addition, what happens when a transformation does affect a figure's size?

In this lesson, you will learn to describe transformations using coordinates. You will also learn about dilations, a transformation that changes the size of a figure.

Goals for This Lesson

- Dilate a figure using a given scale factor.

- Find the scale factor of a dilation given coordinates.

- Describe a transformation using coordinates.

Graded Activities in This Lesson
Lesson Quiz (computer-scored)

Materials
Intermediate Mathematics C: A Reference Guide and Problem Sets, pages 400–405

Optional
calculator

Keywords
center of dilation: a fixed point in which a figure stretches or shrinks with respect to that point

dilation: a transformation that changes the size, but not the shape, of a figure

scale factor: in a dilation, the ratio of the length of a side on the image to the length of its corresponding side on the pre-image

similar figures: figures that are the same shape but not necessarily the same size; congruent figures are also similar

Learn: Dilations [online]
You will describe dilations using scale factors.

Summarize what you learned in this activity.

1. A dilation is a transformation that changes the _____ of a figure, but not its _____.

2. What is the scale factor of a dilation?

3. How can you find the scale factor of a dilation?

4. How can you find the coordinates of the image, given the coordinates of the pre-image, assuming that the center of dilation is the origin?

Learn: Coordinates of Transformations [online]

You will describe transformations using the coordinates of the pre-image and the image.

Summarize what you learned in this activity.

1. How do translations, rotations, and reflections affect the coordinates of figures?

2. How do dilations affect the coordinates of figures?

Worked Examples: Coordinates of Transformations [online]

Use the space below to work through the examples you see in the online screens.

Summary: Transformations and Coordinates [online]

This table summarizes how transformations affect the coordinates of figures.

Transformation	Coordinates of Pre-image	Coordinates of Image
Translation *a* units left or right and *b* units up or down	(x, y)	$(x + a, y + b)$
Reflection across *x*-axis	(x, y)	$(x, -y)$
Reflection across *y*-axis	(x, y)	$(-x, y)$
Rotation 90° clockwise about the origin	(x, y)	$(y, -x)$
Rotation 90° counterclockwise about the origin	(x, y)	$(-y, x)$
Rotation 180° about the origin	(x, y)	$(-x, -y)$
Dilation by a scale factor of *a* with origin as center of dilation	(x, y)	(ax, ay)

Offline Learning: Transformations and Coordinates [offline]
Read pages 400–404 in the reference guide.

Problem Sets
Complete Problems 1–17 odd and 23–26 on pages 404–405.

Lesson Assessment: Transformations and Coordinates Quiz [online]
Go back online to complete the Lesson Quiz.

Student Guide

Transformations and Similarity

A sequence of rigid transformations produces shapes that are congruent. But what if the shapes produced are similar but not congruent? What types of transformations may have occurred? In this lesson, you will determine the sequence of transformations used to produce noncongruent, but similar, shapes.

Goals for This Lesson
- Use transformations to determine whether two figures are similar.

Graded Activities in This Lesson
Lesson Quiz (computer-scored)

Materials
Intermediate Mathematics C: A Reference Guide and Problem Sets, pages 406–411

Optional
calculator

Groundwork: Preparing for the Lesson [online]
You will review finding the scale factor for similar figures.

Learn: Multiple Transformations [online]
You will identify a sequence of transformations to determine whether two figures are similar.

Summarize what you learned in this activity.
1. What type of transformation produces similar figures?

2. How can the coordinates of vertices in the image and the pre-image help you determine whether two figures are similar?

Worked Examples: Try Multiple Transformations [online]

Use the space below to work through the examples you see in the online screens. Use the table to analyze the coordinates if necessary.

Transformation	Coordinates of Pre-image	Coordinates of Image
Translation *a* units left or right and *b* units up or down	(x, y)	$(x + a, y + b)$
Reflection across *x*-axis	(x, y)	$(x, -y)$
Reflection across *y*-axis	(x, y)	$(-x, y)$
Rotation 90° clockwise about the origin	(x, y)	$(y, -x)$
Rotation 90° counterclockwise about the origin	(x, y)	$(-y, x)$
Rotation 180° about the origin	(x, y)	$(-x, -y)$
Dilation by a scale factor of *a* with origin as center of dilation	(x, y)	(ax, ay)

Summary: Transformations and Similarity [online]

Rigid transformations produce congruent figures. Dilations produce figures that are similar, but not congruent.

When a figure is transformed multiple times and dilation is one of the transformations, the final image will be similar to the pre-image.

To determine a sequence of transformations, you can compare and analyze the coordinates of vertices in the image and the pre-image.

Offline Learning: Transformations and Similarity [offline]
Read pages 406–409 in the reference guide.

Problem Sets
Complete Problems 1–17 odd on pages 409–411.

Lesson Assessment: Transformations and Similarity

Quiz [online]
Go back online to complete the Lesson Quiz.

Student Guide

Core Focus: The AA Criterion

Suppose there are two ways to get to the library. One way takes you past historic city buildings, while the other way takes you through a park. Which way would you choose? Often in math there is more than one way to solve a problem. In this lesson, you will learn a new approach to identifying similar triangles.

Goals for This Lesson
- Use the AA criterion to determine whether two triangles are similar.

Graded Activities in This Lesson
There is no graded activity associated with this lesson.

Materials
Intermediate Mathematics C: A Reference Guide and Problem Sets, pages 418–422

Keywords and Pronunciation
congruent angles: angles that have the same measure

similar figures: figures that have the same shape but not necessarily the same size

Learn: Identifying Similar Triangles Using the AA Criterion [online]
Use the space below to take notes during this activity.

Overview

Using the AA Criterion

Summary

Offline Learning: Core Focus: The AA Criterion [offline]
Read pages 412–414.

Problem Sets
Complete Problems 1–6 on pages 414–415.

Student Guide

Unit Review

You have learned to determine whether figures are congruent or only similar; to find missing side lengths and angle measures; to identify and describe transformations, such as reflections, rotations, translations, and dilations, as well as sequences of those transformations; and to use the AA criterion. Now it's time to pull together what you have learned.

Goals for This Lesson

- Identify congruent and similar polygons

- Use congruence to find missing sides or angle measures.

- Use proportions to find missing side lengths for similar figures.

- Determine whether two figures are similar and find a missing side length in a pair of similar figures.

- Find the scale factor for a pair of similar figures with a least one known pair of corresponding sides.

- Determine whether a transformation is a reflection, a rotation, or a translation.

- Experimentally verify the properties of rotations, reflections, and translations.

- Describe a transformation using a sequence of transformations.

- Dilate a figure using a given scale factor.

- Find the scale factor of a dilation.

- Describe a transformation using coordinates.

- Use transformations to determine if two figures are similar.

- Use the AA criterion to determine whether two triangles are similar.

Graded Activities in This Lesson
There is no graded activity associated with this lesson.

Materials
Intermediate Mathematics C: A Reference Guide and Problem Sets, pages 416–417

Optional
calculator

Keywords
center of rotation: the point about which a figure is rotated

congruent angles: angles that have the same measure

congruent polygons: polygons that are the same size and shape

dilation: a transformation that changes the size, but not the shape, of a figure

image: in a transformation, the new figure that results from the transformation

line of reflection: the line that a figure is reflected across

pre-image: the original figure in a transformation

reflection: a transformation of a figure by flipping it across a line or line segment, creating a mirror image of the figure

rotation: a transformation of a figure by turning it about a given point

scale factor: a ratio of one measure to another, where both measures are the same unit of measure

similar figures: figures that have the same shape but not necessarily the same size

similar polygons: polygons that have the same shape, but not necessarily the same size

translation: the movement of a figure along a line, sometimes called a slide

vector: a line segment with a direction indicated with an arrow

Unit Review: Practice Test [online]

The last screen of the Practice Quiz will show you how many times you attempted each problem. For each problem, record your number of attempts below. Complete the activities and reference guide problems that correspond with the Practice Quiz problems that took you more than one attempt. Check off the review activities and review problems as you complete them.

Problem 1
Attempts: _____
□ Complete review activities online.
□ Complete Problems 7–12 on page 378.

Problem 2
Attempts: _____
□ Complete review activities online.
□ Complete Problems 21–25 on pages 379–380.

Problem 3
Attempts: _____
□ Complete review activities online.
□ Complete Problems 1–2 on page 384.

Problem 4
Attempts: _____
□ Complete review activities online.
□ Complete Problems 7–12 on page 385.

Problem 5
Attempts: _____
□ Complete review activities online.
□ Complete Problems 22–27 on page 392.

Problem 6
Attempts: _____
□ Complete review activities online.
□ Complete Problems 1–4 on pages 395–396.

Problem 7
Attempts: _____
□ Complete review activities online.
□ Complete Problems 1–6 on page 399.

Problem 8

Attempts: _____

☐ Complete review activities online.

☐ Complete Problems 19–24 on page 405.

Problem 9

Attempts: _____

☐ Complete review activities online.

☐ Complete Problems 7–13 on page 410–411.

Problem 10

Attempts: _____

☐ Complete review activities online.

☐ Complete Problems 1–5 on page 414–415.

Offline Learning: Transformations, Congruence, and Similarity Review [offline]

Complete all the Chapter Review problems on pages 416–417. Use the Topic Lookup at the bottom of page 417 to review topics for any problems that were difficult for you.

Student Guide

Transformations, Congruence, and Similarity Test

You have learned to determine whether figures are congruent or similar; to find missing side lengths and angle measures; to identify and describe transformations, such as reflections, rotations, translations, and dilations, as well as sequences of those transformations; and to use the AA criterion. Now it's time to take the Unit Test. This Unit Test has two parts—one part that will be scored by the computer and one part that your Learning Coach will score. You will complete the computer-scored part first.

Goals for This Lesson

- Identify congruent and similar polygons

- Use congruence to find missing side or angle measures.

- Use proportions to find missing side lengths for similar figures.

- Determine whether two figures are similar and find a missing side length in a pair of similar figures.

- Find the scale factor for a pair of similar figures with at least one known pair of corresponding sides.

- Determine whether a transformation is a reflection, a rotation, or a translation.

- Experimentally verify the properties of rotations, reflections, and translations.

- Describe a transformation using a sequence of transformations.

- Dilate a figure using a given scale factor.

- Find the scale factor of a dilation.

- Describe a transformation using coordinates.

- Use the AA criterion to determine whether two triangles are similar.

Graded Activities in This Lesson

Transformations, Congruence, and Similarity Test, Part 1

Transformations, Congruence, and Similarity Test, Part 2

Unit Test: Transformations, Congruence, and Similarity Test, Part 1 [online]

This part of the Unit Test is online. It will be scored by the computer.

Unit Test: Transformations, Congruence, and Similarity Test, Part 2 [offline]

This part of the Unit Test is offline.

1. Complete each question on your own. Show all your work.

2. Submit this part to your Learning Coach for a grade.

Student Guide

Extended Problems: Real-World Application

You can create artistic designs by translating, reflecting, rotating, and dilating geometric shapes. Study the design in the online screen. How many geometric transformations do you see? In this lesson, you'll complete Extended Problems: Real-World Application for the Transformations, Congruence, and Similarity unit.

Goals for This Lesson
- Apply mathematical knowledge and skills to evaluate and analyze real-world situations.

Graded Activities in This Lesson
Extended Problems: Real-World Application

Extended Problems: Real-World Application [offline]

You will complete a graded assignment that focuses on a real-world application of math.

Your Learning Coach will grade this assignment.

- **Complete** the assignment on your own.
- **Submit** the completed assignment to your Learning Coach.

Student Guide

Rational Numbers

On the stock market yesterday, shares of Ramble-On Cellular stock rose 1.75 points and shares of Musikdef Electronics stock grew 1.63 points. Are you able to determine which stock showed the greater increase? A thorough knowledge of the properties of rational numbers can help you answer not only this question but also a multitude of others that you will encounter in this lesson and throughout your adult life. Other areas in which the use of rational numbers has a significant role include drafting and design in manufacturing and industry, automotive and architectural design, and health and fitness benefits.

Goals for This Lesson
- Find a rational number between two given rational numbers.
- Order rational numbers.
- Express rational numbers as fractions, decimals, and percents.

Graded Activities in This Lesson
Lesson Quiz (computer-scored)

Materials
Intermediate Mathematics C: A Reference Guide and Problem Sets, pages 423–426

Optional
calculator

Keywords and Pronunciation
integers: all positive and negative whole numbers including zero {…−2, −1, 0, 1, 2, …}

rational number: any number that can be expressed as a ratio (*a/b*) where *a* and *b* are integers and *b* is nonzero

Skills Update: Practice Your Math Skills [online]
Complete the Skills Update online.

Groundwork: Preparing for the Lesson [online]
You will review how to compare integers and write numbers in various forms.

Learn: Order Those Numbers [online]

You will learn to order and compare rational numbers.

Summarize what you learned in this activity.

1. Define rational number.

2. Describe two ways to compare rational numbers.

3. What is the density property of rational numbers?

Worked Examples: Try Ordering Rational Numbers [online]

Use the space below to work through the examples you see in the online screens.

MathCast: Rational Numbers Between Rational Numbers [online]

View the video to see how to solve a typical problem.

Summary: Rational Numbers [online]

You can compare two rational numbers by comparing cross products.

Between any two rational numbers, you can always find another rational number.

Every rational number can be written as a quotient of two integers.

Offline Learning: Rational Numbers [offline]

Read pages 423–425 in the reference guide.

Problem Sets

Complete Problems 1–27 odd and 28 on page 426.

Extra Practice (optional)

Complete Problems 2–26 even on page 426 for extra practice.

Lesson Assessment: Rational Numbers Quiz [online]

Go back online to complete the Lesson Quiz.

Student Guide

Terminating and Repeating Decimals

When constructing a skyscraper, it is important to create a strong foundation. The process for creating this foundation is straightforward, but there are certain shortcuts that can make the process more efficient, and there are certain materials that can make the foundation stronger. In this lesson, you will examine a concept that is a foundation of algebra. At first, you might think this concept,that there are numbers between numbers, is obvious. However, this property and the techniques used to explore and show it are interesting and essential to algebra.

Goals for This Lesson

- Express a fraction as a decimal.

- Express a decimal as the ratio of two integers.

- Find a rational number between two given rational numbers.

Graded Activities in This Lesson

Lesson Quiz (computer-scored)

Materials

Intermediate Mathematics C: A Reference Guide and Problem Sets, pages 427–430

Optional

calculator

Keywords and Pronunciation

nonterminating decimals: decimals that do not terminate, or end

rational number: any number that can be expressed as a ratio (*a/b*) where *a* and *b* are integers and *b* is nonzero

terminating decimals: decimals that have a finite number of nonzero digits

---

Skills Update: Practice Your Math Skills [online]

Complete the Skills Update online.

Learn: Terminating and Repeating Decimals [online]

In this activity, you will learn how to write fractions as decimals. You will also learn about terminating and repeating decimals.

Summarize what you learned in this activity.

1. How is a repeating decimal different from a terminating decimal?

---

2. What is the process for writing a fraction as a decimal? How can you tell if the decimal is terminating or repeating?

Worked Examples: Try Working with Decimals [online]
Use the space below to work through the examples you see in the online screens.

Learn: Numbers Between Numbers [online]
In this activity, you will learn about the density of numbers.

Explain the process for finding a rational number between a given fraction and repeating decimal.

Worked Examples: Try Finding a Rational Number [online]
Use the space below to work through the examples you see in the online screens.

Summary: Terminating and Repeating Decimals [online]
Decimals can be terminating or nonterminating.

A nonterminating decimal that has a repeating pattern of digits after the decimal point is a repeating decimal.

Terminating and repeating decimals make up all rational numbers.

Between any two rational numbers are an infinite number of rational numbers.

Offline Learning: Terminating and Repeating Decimals [offline]
Read pages 427–429 in the reference guide.

Problem Sets
Complete Problems 1–29 odd on page 430.

Extra Practice (optional)
Complete Problems 2–28 even on page 430 for extra practice.

Lesson Assessment: Terminating and Repeating Decimals Quiz [online]
Go back online to complete the Lesson Quiz.

Student Guide
Understanding Irrational Numbers

The real number system is made up of two major categories of numbers: rational numbers and irrational numbers. Rational numbers are numbers that can be expressed as fractions, and irrational numbers are numbers that cannot be expressed as fractions. In this lesson, you will learn how to determine whether a number is rational or irrational.

Goals for This Lesson
- Classify a number as rational or irrational.

Graded Activities in This Lesson
Lesson Quiz (computer-scored)

Materials
Intermediate Mathematics C: A Reference Guide and Problem Sets, pages 431–434

Optional
calculator

Keywords
irrational number: any real number that cannot be written in the form *a/b* for any integers *a* and *b*; in decimal form, all irrational numbers are nonterminating and nonrepeating; the set of irrational numbers is denoted by $\mathcal{I}$

simple fraction: a fraction which has an integer in both the numerator and the denominator

Learn: Irrational Numbers [online]
You will learn how to determine whether a number is rational or irrational.

Summarize what you learned in this activity.

1. List the types of numbers that are classified as rational numbers.

2. What are irrational numbers?

Worked Examples: Try Irrational Numbers [online]

Use the space below to work through the examples you see in the online screens.

Summary: Understanding Irrational Numbers [online]

Real numbers are made up of rational and irrational numbers. Irrational numbers are nonterminating, nonrepeating decimals.

Offline Learning: Understanding Irrational Numbers [offline]

Read pages 431–433 in the reference guide.

Problem Sets

Complete Problems 1–19 odd on pages 433–434.

Extra Practice (optional)
Complete Problems 2–18 even on page 433.

Lesson Assessment: Understanding Irrational Numbers Quiz [online]

Go back online to complete the Lesson Quiz.

Student Guide

Rational Square Roots

A rational number is a number you can write as the ratio of two integers *a/b*, where *a* and *b* are integers and *b* is not equal to 0.

Are square roots rational or irrational? In this lesson, you will learn how to determine when a square root is rational, and how to solve equations involving rational square roots.

Goals for This Lesson
- Find square roots of a perfect square.
- Solve a simple equation with squares.

Graded Activities in This Lesson
Lesson Quiz (computer-scored)

Materials
Intermediate Mathematics C: A Reference Guide and Problem Sets, pages 435–437

Optional
calculator

Keywords and Pronunciation
perfect square: a rational number whose square root is also a rational number

principal square root: the nonnegative square root, indicated by the square root sign

radical sign: the symbol used to denote the square root of a number

rational square root: a square root that is a rational number

square root: a factor of a number that when multiplied by itself results in the number; the nonnegative square root is called the principal square root and is indicated by the square root sign

Groundwork: Preparing for the Lesson [online]
You will review how to find the square of a number.

Learn: What Is a Square Root? [online]
You will learn how to find the square roots of perfect squares and how to solve equations involving perfect squares.

1. Define the square root of a number.

2. Is 225 a perfect square? Explain.

3. What are the square roots of 225?

4. What is the principal square root of 225?

5. Describe how you can use transformations and square roots to solve the equation $2x^2 - 4 = 12$.

Worked Examples: Rational Square Roots [online]
Use the space below to work through the examples you see in the online screens.

MathCast: Solve an Equation [online]
View the video to see how to solve a typical problem.

Summary: Rational Square Roots [online]
A square root is a factor of a number that, when multiplied by itself, results in the number.

If a square root of a number is a rational number, it is called a rational square root.

The principal square root is the nonnegative square root of a number.

You can solve equations with square roots by using the square root property.

Offline Learning: Rational Square Roots [offline]

Read pages 435–437 in the reference guide.

Problem Sets

Complete Problems 1–25 odd on page 437.

Extra Practice (optional)
Complete Problems 2–26 even on page 437.

Lesson Assessment: Rational Square Roots Quiz [online]

Go back online to complete the Lesson Quiz.

Student Guide

Irrational Square Roots, Part 1

Throughout history, people have used a variety of methods and tools to find square roots of numbers. These methods and tools include paper-and-pencil algorithms, the "binary chop" method, slide rules, published tables of values, and calculators. Sometimes a mental estimation also works well. In this lesson, you will learn about irrational square roots and how to simplify and approximate them.

Goals for This Lesson

- Approximate a square root to the nearest tenth.

- Write the square root of a positive whole number in simplified radical form.

Graded Activities in This Lesson

Lesson Quiz (computer-scored)

Materials

Intermediate Mathematics C: A Reference Guide and Problem Sets, pages 439–441

calculator

Keywords

Irrational number: any real number that cannot be written in the form *a/b* for any integers *a* and *b*; in decimal form, all irrational numbers are nonterminating and nonrepeating; the set of irrational numbers is denoted by *I*

Learn: Simplifying Radicals [online]

You will learn how to use the product property of radicals to simplify irrational square roots.

Summarize what you learned in this activity.
1. What is the product property of radicals?

2. Simplify $\sqrt{28}$.

Worked Examples: Try Simplifying Radicals [online]

Use the space below to work through the examples you see in the online screens.

Summary: Irrational Square Roots, Part 1 [online]

You can use the product property of radicals to simplify a radical expression if the radicand has a set of factors in which at least one factor is a perfect square.

You can use a calculator to approximate the value of an irrational square root.

Offline Learning: Irrational Square Roots, Part 1 [offline]

Read pages 439–440 in the reference guide.

Problem Sets

Complete Problems 1–19 odd on page 441.

Extra Practice (optional)
Complete Problems 2–20 even on page 441.

Lesson Assessment: Irrational Square Roots, Part 1

Quiz [online]

Go back online to complete the Lesson Quiz.

Student Guide

Irrational Square Roots, Part 2

Suppose you have a square garden with an area of 2200 ft^2, and you want to put fencing around the garden. How much fencing will you need? Knowing how to calculate a square root is essential for solving this problem.

Goals for This Lesson
- Solve a word problem involving square roots.

Graded Activities in This Lesson
Lesson Quiz (computer-scored)

Materials
Intermediate Mathematics C: A Reference Guide and Problem Sets, pages 440–441

calculator

Learn: Problem Solving [online]

You will learn how to solve area problems using square roots.

Summarize what you learned in this activity.

1. How can you find the length of the side of a square-shaped region if you are given the region's area?

2. How can you find the perimeter of a square-shaped region if you are given the region's area?

Worked Examples: Try Problem Solving [online]

Use the space below to work through the examples you see in the online screens.

MathCast: Solve a Problem [online]

View the video to see how to solve a typical problem.

Summary: Irrational Square Roots, Part 2 [online]

Some real-world applications include a square surface. If you know the area of the square, you can use the square root property to calculate the length of 1 side.

Offline Learning: Irrational Square Roots, Part 2 [offline]

Read page 440 in the reference guide.

Problem Sets

Complete Problems 21–25 on page 441.

Lesson Assessment: Irrational Square Roots, Part 2 Quiz

[online]
Go back online to complete the Lesson Quiz.

Student Guide

Core Focus: Approximations of Irrationals

One way to approximate the value of an irrational square root is to use a calculator and round to the indicated place value. But suppose you didn't have a calculator handy. How could you approximate the square root? In this situation, you would have to rely on your knowledge of rational square roots.

In this lesson, you will learn how to use rational square roots to estimate the value of irrational square roots.

Goals for This Lesson
- Approximate irrational square roots.

Graded Activities in This Lesson
Lesson Quiz (computer-graded)

Materials
Intermediate Mathematics C: A Reference Guide and Problem Sets, pages 442–443

Groundwork: Preparing for the Lesson [online]
You will find the two perfect squares that a given number lies between.

Learn: Approximating Irrational Square Roots [offline]
Use the spaces below to take notes during this activity.

Approximating Irrational Square Roots

Summary

Worked Examples: Try Approximating Irrational Square Roots

[online]
Use the space below to work through the examples you see in the online screens.

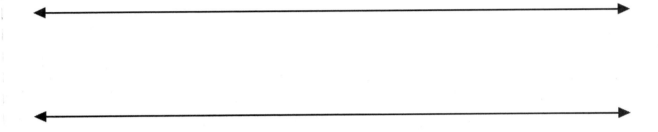

Offline Learning: Core Focus: Approximations of Irrationals [offline]
Read pages 442–443.

Problem Sets
Complete Problems 1–7 on page 443.

Lesson Assessment: Core Focus: Approximations of Irrationals Quiz [online]
Go back online to complete the Lesson Quiz.

Student Guide

Cube Roots

The opposite of squaring is finding a square root. But what's the opposite of cubing?

In this lesson, you will learn how to find cube roots. You will find that knowledge about simplifying square roots will help you here.

Goals for the Lesson

- Simplify cube roots.

Graded Activities in This Lesson

Lesson Quiz (computer-scored)

Materials

Intermediate Mathematics C: A Reference Guide and Problem Sets, pages 444–445

Optional

calculator

Keywords and Pronunciation

cube root: a number that when multiplied by itself three times equals a given number

---

Learn: Cube Roots [online]

You will learn to find the cube roots of numbers.

Summarize what you learned in this activity.

1. What does the symbol $\sqrt[3]{}$ mean?

2. Can you find the odd root of a negative number? Can you find the even root of a negative number? Explain.

3. Simplify $\sqrt[3]{128}$.

Worked Examples: Try Cube Roots [online]
Use the space below to work through the examples you see in the online screens.

Summary: Cube Roots [online]
Finding the cube root of a number is the opposite of raising a number to the third power.

It is possible to find an odd root of a negative number, although it is not possible to find an even root of a negative number.

Simplify a cube root expression by factoring out any perfect cubes within the radical and taking their cube root.

Offline Learning: Cube Roots [offline]
Read pages 444–445 in the reference guide.

Problem Sets
Complete Problems 1–9, 14, and 15 on page 445.

Lesson Assessment: Cube Roots Quiz [online]
Go back online to complete the Lesson Quiz.

Student Guide

Using Square Roots to Solve Equations

So far, you've learned how to solve equations using transformations and how to find square roots involving positive real numbers and variables. Now it's time to put the two ideas together. In this lesson, you will learn how to solve equations using transformations and square roots.

Goals for This Lesson
- Solve an equation that involves a rational square root.

- Solve an equation that involves an irrational square root

Graded Activities in This Lesson
Lesson Quiz (computer-scored)

Materials
Intermediate Mathematics C: A Reference Guide and Problem Sets, pages 446–448

Optional
calculator

Groundwork: Preparing for the Lesson [online]
You will review square roots.

Learn: Using Square Roots to Solve Equations [online]
You will combine what you have learned about finding square roots with what you have learned about solving equations.

Summarize what you learned in this activity.

1. How many solutions does the equation $x^2 = 144$ have? Why?

2. What are the steps involved in solving the equation $2x^2 - 21 = 123$?

Worked Examples: Try Using Square Roots to Solve Equations [online]

Use the space below to work through the examples you see in the online screens.

Summary: Using Square Roots to Solve Equations [online]

To solve equations using square roots, use transformations to isolate the variable and take the square root of both sides of the equation.

Remember that all positive numbers have a positive and a negative square root.

Offline Learning: Using Square Roots to Solve Equations [offline]

Read pages 446–447 in the reference guide.

Problem Sets

Complete Problems 1–17 odd and 23–25 odd on page 448.

Extra Practice (optional)

Complete Problems 2–18 even and 22–26 even on page 448.

Lesson Assessment: Using Square Roots to Solve Equations

Quiz [online]

Go back online to complete the Lesson Quiz.

Student Guide

Core Focus: Using Cube Roots to Solve Equations

The opposite of squaring a number is to take the square root. Therefore, to solve equations in the form $x^2 = a$, you must take the square roots of both sides. Similarly, the opposite of cubing a number is to take the cube root.

In this lesson, you will learn how to solve equations in the form $x^3 = a$.

Goals for This Lesson
- Solve an equation that involves a cube root.

Graded Activities in This Lesson
There is no graded activity associated with this lesson.

Materials
Intermediate Mathematics C: A Reference Guide and Problem Sets, pages 449–451

Learn: Using Cube Roots to Solve Equations [online]
Use the space below to take notes during this activity.

Overview

Solving Equations with Cube Roots

Solving Real-World Problems with Cube Roots

Summary

Offline Learning: Core Focus: Using Cube Roots to Solve Equations [offline]

Read pages 449–450.

Problem Sets

Complete Problems 1–9 on page 451.

Student Guide

Unit Review

In this unit, you learned how to determine whether numbers are rational or irrational. You learned how to simplify and estimate rational and irrational square roots, and you learned how to solve equations that involve rational or irrational square roots. In addition, you learned how to simplify expressions and solve equations that involve cube roots. Now it's time to pull together what you have learned.

Goals for This Lesson
- Order rational numbers.
- Express a fraction as a decimal.
- Find a rational number between two given rational numbers.
- Find a number that is between two rational numbers.
- Express a decimal as the ratio of two integers.
- Classify a number as rational or irrational.
- Find square roots of a perfect square.
- Solve a simple equation with squares.
- Approximate a square root to the nearest tenth.
- Write the square root of a positive whole number in simplified radical form.
- Solve a word problem involving square roots.
- Approximate irrational square roots
- Simplify cube roots.
- Solve an equation that involves a rational square root.
- Solve an equation that involves an irrational square root.
- Solve an equation that involves a cube root.

Graded Activities in This Lesson
There is no graded activity associated with this lesson.

Materials
Intermediate Mathematics C: A Reference Guide and Problem Sets, pages 452–453

Optional
calculator

Keywords
cube root: a number that when multiplied by itself three times equals a given number

irrational number: any real number that cannot be written in the form *a/b* for any integers *a* and *b*; in decimal form, all irrational numbers are nonterminating and nonrepeating; the set of irrational numbers is denoted by *I*

perfect square: a whole number whose square root is an integer

principal square root: the nonnegative square root, indicated by the square root sign

rational number: any number that can be expressed as a ratio (a/b) where a and b are integers and b is nonzero

rational square root: a square root that is a rational number

simple fraction: a fraction that has an integer in both the numerator and the denominator

square root: a factor of a number that when multiplied by itself results in the number; the nonnegative square root is called the principal square root and is indicated by the square root sign

Unit Review: Practice Quiz [online]

The last screen of the Practice Quiz will show you how many times you attempted each problem. For each problem, record your number of attempts below. Complete the activities and reference guide problems that correspond with the Practice Quiz problems that took you more than one attempt. Check off the review activities and review problems as you complete them.

Problem 1
Attempts: _____
□ Complete review activities online.
□ Complete Problems 2–3 on page 426.

Problem 2
Attempts: _____
□ Complete review activities online.
□ Complete Problems 1–5 on page 437.

Problem 3
Attempts: _____
□ Complete review activities online.
□ Complete Problems 11–20 on page 437.

Problem 4
Attempts: _____
□ Complete review activities online.
□ Complete Problems 11–20 on page 441.

Problem 5
Attempts: _____
□ Complete review activities online.
□ Complete Problems 1–9 on page 445.

Problem 6
Attempts: _____
□ Complete review activities online.
□ Complete Problems 1–9 on page 445.

Problem 7
Attempts: _____
□ Complete review activities online.
□ Complete Problems 1–9 on page 445.

Problem 8

Attempts: _____

☐ Complete review activities online.
☐ Complete Problems 9–17 on page 448.

Problem 9

Attempts: _____

☐ Complete review activities online.
☐ Complete Problems 9–17 on page 448.

Problem 10

Attempts: _____

☐ Complete review activities online.
☐ Complete Problems 1–6 on page 451.

Offline Learning: Irrational Numbers Review [offline]

Complete all the Chapter Review problems on pages 452–453. Use the Topic Lookup at the bottom of page 453 to review topics for any problems that were difficult for you.

Student Guide

Irrational Numbers Test

You have learned how to order and express rational numbers in different forms, how to identify rational and irrational numbers, how to estimate and simplify square roots, how to solve equations and word problems involving square roots, and how to simplify expressions and solve equations involving cube roots. Now it's time to take the Unit Test. This Unit Test has two parts—one part that will be scored by the computer and one part that your Learning Coach will score. You will complete the computer-scored part first.

Goals for This Lesson
- Find square roots of a perfect square.
- Determine whether a square root is rational or irrational.
- Solve a word problem involving square roots.
- Put an expression that does not involve fractions into simplified radical form.
- Find a rational number between two given rational numbers.
- Express a decimal as the ratio of two integers.
- Simplify variable expressions involving cube and higher roots.
- Order rational numbers
- Approximate an irrational square root.
- Solve equations or word problems involving square roots.
- Approximate irrational square roots.
- Simplify cube roots.
- Solve an equation that involves a cube root.

Graded Activities in This Lesson
Irrational Numbers Test, Part 1

Irrational Numbers Test, Part 2

Unit Test: Irrational Numbers Test, Part 1 [online]
This part of the Unit Test is online. It will be scored by the computer.

Unit Test: Irrational Numbers Test, Part 2 [offline]
This part of the Unit Test is offline.

1. Complete each question on your own. Show all your work.
2. Submit this part to your Learning Coach for a grade.

Student Guide

Extended Problems: Reasoning

In this lesson, you'll complete Extended Problems: Reasoning for the Irrational Numbers unit.

Goals for This Lesson
- Analyze complex problems using mathematical knowledge and skills.

Graded Activities in This Lesson

Extended Problems: Reasoning

Extended Problems: Reasoning [offline]

You will complete a graded assignment that focuses on reasoning in math.

Your Learning Coach will score this assignment.

- **Complete** the assignment on your own.
- **Submit** the completed assignment to your Learning Coach.

Student Guide

Using the Pythagorean Theorem

Thousands of years ago, the ancient Babylonians discovered that a special relationship exists among the sides of a right triangle. This special relationship later became known as the Pythagorean theorem. The theorem got its name from the Greek mathematician Pythagoras, the first person to prove this relationship true. It is an extremely important theorem that you will see repeatedly throughout mathematics.

So what is the Pythagorean theorem? This lesson will teach you.

Goals for This Lesson
- Use the Pythagorean Theorem to find a missing length in a right triangle.
- Use the converse of the Pythagorean Theorem to determine whether a triangle with given side lengths is a right triangle.

Materials
Intermediate Mathematics C: A Reference Guide and Problem Sets, pages 459–463

Optional
calculator

Keywords
converse: the statement that is formed when the "if" and "then" of an original statement are interchanged

hypotenuse: the side opposite the right angle in a right triangle

legs of a right triangle: the two sides forming the right angle

Pythagorean Theorem: in any right triangle, the square of the length of the hypotenuse equals the sum of the squares of the lengths of the legs

theorem: a statement that is shown to be true by use of a logically developed argument

Skills Update: Practice Your Math Skills [online]
Complete the Skills Update online.

Groundwork: Preparing for the Lesson [online]
You will review square roots.

Learn: Pythagorean Theorem [online]

You will learn the Pythagorean Theorem and its converse.

Summarize what you learned in this activity.

1. If a triangle has legs *a* and *b* and hypotenuse *c*, what does the Pythagorean theorem state?

2. What does the converse of the Pythagorean theorem state?

Worked Examples: Try Using the Pythagorean Theorem [online]

Use the space below to work through the examples you see in the online screens.

MathCast: Finding the Hypotenuse [online]

View the video to see how to solve a typical problem.

Summary: Using the Pythagorean Theorem [online]

You can use the Pythagorean theorem to do the following:

- Find the length of 1 side of a right triangle when given the lengths of the other sides.
- Determine the lengths of segments with irrational measures.

You can use the converse of the Pythagorean theorem to determine whether three given numbers can represent the lengths of the sides of a right triangle.

Offline Learning: Using the Pythagorean Theorem [offline]

Read pages 459–461 in the reference guide.

Problem Sets

Complete Problems 1–21 odd on pages 462–463.

Extra Practice (optional)
Complete Problems 2–20 even on pages 462–463.

Lesson Assessment: Using the Pythagorean Theorem Quiz [online]

Go back online to complete the Lesson Quiz.

Student Guide

Proofs of the Pythagorean Theorem

The Pythagorean theorem tells you that if a triangle is a right triangle, then the sum of the squares of the legs of the triangle equals the square of the hypotenuse. Can you prove this to be true? In this lesson, you will learn how to use models to demonstrate the Pythagorean theorem.

Goals for This Lesson

- Use models to show the Pythagorean theorem.

- Use models to show the converse of the Pythagorean theorem.

Graded Activities in This Lesson

Lesson Quiz (computer-scored)

Materials

Intermediate Mathematics C: A Reference Guide and Problem Sets, pages 464–466

Optional

calculator

Learn: Proving the Pythagorean Theorem [online]

You will learn how to use models to demonstrate the Pythagorean theorem and how to use models to apply the converse of the Pythagorean theorem.

Summarize what you learned in this activity.

1. How can you use this model to demonstrate the Pythagorean theorem?

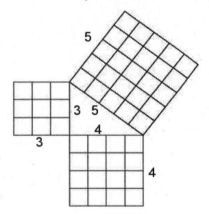

Worked Examples: Proving the Pythagorean Theorem [online]

Use the space below to work through the examples you see in the online screens.

Summary: Proofs of the Pythagorean Theorem [online]

You can use models to demonstrate the Pythagorean theorem, and you can use models to apply the converse of the Pythagorean theorem to show that a triangle is a right triangle.

Offline Learning: Proofs of the Pythagorean Theorem [offline]

Read pages 464–466 in the reference guide.

Problem Sets

Complete Problems 1–7 on page 466.

Lesson Assessment: Proofs of the Pythagorean Theorem
Quiz [offline]

Go back online to complete the Lesson Quiz.

Student Guide

Applications of the Pythagorean Theorem

The Pythagorean theorem has many practical uses in everyday situations. For instance, suppose a 20 ft ladder leans against a building so that the base of the ladder is 15 ft from the building. Could you figure out how high above the ground the ladder touches the building? This type of problem would require you to use the Pythagorean theorem.

In this lesson, you'll learn how to solve real-world problems that use the Pythagorean theorem.

Goals for This Lesson
- Use the Pythagorean Theorem to solve a word problem.

Graded Activities in This Lesson
Lesson Quiz (computer-scored)

Materials
Intermediate Mathematics C: A Reference Guide and Problem Sets, pages 467–469

Optional
calculator

Groundwork: Preparing for the Lesson [online]
You will use the Pythagorean theorem to find missing side lengths in right triangles.

Learn: Putting Pythagoras to Work [online]
You will learn how to use the Pythagorean theorem to solve word problems.

Summarize what you learned in this activity.
1. Why is it important to draw a diagram when solving word problems that involve the Pythagorean theorem?

Worked Examples: Try Putting Pythagoras to Work [online]
Use the space below to work through the examples you see in the online screens.

MathCast: Using the Pythagorean Theorem [online]

View the video to see how to solve a typical problem.

Summary: Applications of the Pythagorean Theorem [online]

You can use the Pythagorean theorem to solve real-world problems that require you to find a missing side length of a right triangle.

Offline Learning: Applications of the Pythagorean Theorem [offline]

Read pages 467–468 in the reference guide.

Problem Sets

Complete Problems 1–13 odd on pages 468–469.

Extra Practice (optional)
Complete Problems 2–14 even on pages 468–469.

Lesson Assessment: Applications of the Pythagorean Theorem Quiz [online]

Go back online to complete the Lesson Quiz.

Student Guide

Distances with the Pythagorean Theorem

Suppose you wanted to find the length of a horizontal line segment in the coordinate plane. You would find the difference between the *x*-coordinates of the endpoints and take the absolute value of the difference. If you wanted to find the length of a vertical line segment, you would find the difference between the *y*-coordinates of the endpoints and take the absolute value of that difference.

But what would you do if you wanted to find the length of a segment that was neither horizontal nor vertical? You couldn't simplify subtract endpoints. Instead, you would use the Pythagorean theorem. How? This lesson will teach you.

Goals for This Lesson
* Use the Pythagorean theorem to find diagonal distances in the coordinate plane.

Graded Activities in This Lesson
Lesson Quiz (computer-scored)

Materials
Intermediate Mathematics C: A Reference Guide and Problem Sets, pages 470–474

Optional
calculator

Groundwork: Preparing for the Lesson [online]
You will find the lengths of horizontal and vertical line segments in the coordinate plane.

Learn: Distance in the Coordinate Plane [online]
You will learn how to use the Pythagorean theorem to find the length of a nonhorizontal, nonvertical line segment in the coordinate plane.

Summarize what you learned in this activity.

> How can you use the Pythagorean theorem to find the length of a nonhorizontal, nonvertical line segment in the coordinate plane?

Worked Examples: Try Distance in the Coordinate Plane [online]
Use the space below to work through the examples you see in the online screens.

Summary: Distances with the Pythagorean Theorem [online]

When a segment is neither horizontal nor vertical, you can think of the segment as the hypotenuse of a right triangle. You can find the length of the segment by using the Pythagorean theorem.

You can extend this concept to finding the distance between two points and the perimeter of polygons in the coordinate plane.

Offline Learning: Distances with the Pythagorean Theorem [offline]

Read pages 470–473 in the reference guide.

Problem Sets

Complete Problems 1–17 odd on pages 473–474.

Extra Practice (optional)
Complete Problems 2–18 even on pages 473–474.

Lesson Assessment: Distances with the Pythagorean Theorem Quiz [online]

Go back online to complete the Lesson Quiz.

Student Guide

Core Focus: Pythagorean Theorem in 3-D

The Pythagorean theorem is a useful tool for finding missing measures. The key is to identify a right triangle in a figure that includes the missing measure.

When you use the Pythagorean theorem to find missing measures in the coordinate plane, you're applying it to two-dimensional figures. However, the world we live in is three-dimensional.

You can use the Pythagorean theorem to find missing measures in three-dimensional figures too, but to do so, you must identify right triangles in those figures that may not be immediately obvious to you. This lesson will teach you how to find these triangles.

Goals for This Lesson
• Use the Pythagorean theorem to solve problems involving 3-dimensional objects.

Graded Activities in This Lesson
Lesson Quiz (computer-graded)

Materials
Intermediate Mathematics C: A Reference Guide and Problem Sets, pages 475–477

Optional
calculator

Learn: Pythagorean Theorem in 3-D [online]
Use the space below to take notes during this activity.

Using the Pythagorean Theorem in 3-D

Summary

Worked Examples: Try Pythagorean Theorem in 3-D [online]

Use the space below to work through the examples you see in the online screens.

Offline Learning: Core Focus: Pythagorean Theorem in 3-D [offline]

Read pages 475–477.

Problem Sets

Complete Problems 1–4 on page 477.

Lesson Assessment: Core Focus: Pythagorean Theorem in 3-D Quiz [online]

Go back online to complete the Lesson Quiz.

Student Guide

Core Focus: More Pythagorean Applications

There are many types of problems that can be solved by using the Pythagorean theorem. In this lesson, you will learn how to apply the Pythagorean theorem to problems involving area.

Goals for This Lesson
- Use the Pythagorean theorem to solve area problems.

Graded Activities in This Lesson
There is no graded activity associated with this lesson.

Materials
Intermediate Mathematics C: A Reference Guide and Problem Sets, pages 478–479

Learn: **Pythagorean Theorem and Area Problems** [online]
Use the space below to take notes during this activity.

Overview

Using the Pythagorean Theorem to Solve Area Problems

Summary

Offline Learning: Core Focus: More Pythagorean Applications [offline]

Read pages 478–479.

Problem Sets

Complete Problems 1–3 on page 479.

Student Guide

Unit Review

You have learned how to use the Pythagorean theorem to solve various types of problems in two and three dimensions. Now it's time to pull together what you have learned.

Goals for This Lesson
- Use the Pythagorean Theorem to find a missing length in a right triangle.
- Use the converse of the Pythagorean Theorem to determine whether a triangle with given side lengths is a right triangle.
- Explain a proof of the Pythagorean theorem and its converse.
- Use the Pythagorean Theorem to solve a word problem.
- Use the Pythagorean theorem to find diagonal distances in the coordinate plane.
- Use the Pythagorean theorem to find distances in 3-dimensional objects.
- Use the Pythagorean theorem to solve area problems.

Graded Activities in This Lesson
There is no graded activity associated with this lesson.

Materials
Intermediate Mathematics C: A Reference Guide and Problem Sets, pages 480–481

Optional
calculator

Unit Review: Practice Quiz [online]
The last screen of the Practice Quiz will show you how many times you attempted each problem. For each problem, record your number of attempts below. Complete the activities and reference guide problems that correspond with the Practice Quiz problems that took you more than one attempt. Check off the review activities and review problems as you complete them.

Problem 1
Attempts: _____
□ Complete review activities online.
□ Complete Problems 1–8 on page 462.

Problem 2
Attempts: _____
□ Complete review activities online.
□ Complete Problems 1–8 on page 462.

Problem 3
Attempts: _____
□ Complete review activities online.
□ Complete Problems 9–15 on page 463.

Problem 4
Attempts: _____
□ Complete review activities online.
□ Complete Problems 1–5 on page 468.

Problem 5
Attempts: _____
□ Complete review activities online.
□ Complete Problems 1–5 on page 468.

Problem 6
Attempts: _____
□ Complete review activities online.
□ Complete Problems 1–6 on page 473.

Problem 7
Attempts: _____
□ Complete review activities online.
□ Complete Problems 7–14 on page 474.

Problem 8
Attempts: _____
□ Complete review activities online.
□ Complete Problems 1–2 on page 477.

Problem 9
Attempts: _____
□ Complete review activities online.
□ Complete Problems 1–2 on page 479.

Offline Learning: The Pythagorean Theorem Review [offline]

Complete all the Chapter Review problems on pages 480–481. Use the Topic Lookup at the bottom of page 481 to review topics for any problems that were difficult for you.

Student Guide

The Pythagorean Theorem Test

You have learned how to solve various types of problems using the Pythagorean theorem. Now it's time to take the Unit Test. This Unit Test has two parts—one part that will be scored by the computer and one part that your Learning Coach will score. You will complete the computer-scored part first.

Goals for This Lesson
- Use the Pythagorean Theorem to find a missing length in a right triangle.
- Use the converse of the Pythagorean Theorem to determine whether a triangle with given side lengths is a right triangle.
- Explain a proof of the Pythagorean theorem and its converse.
- Use the Pythagorean Theorem to solve a word problem.
- Use the Pythagorean theorem to find diagonal distances in the coordinate plane.
- Use the Pythagorean theorem to find distances in 3-dimensional objects.
- Use the Pythagorean theorem to solve area problems.

Graded Activities in This Lesson
The Pythagorean Theorem Test, Part 1

The Pythagorean Theorem Test, Part 2

Unit Test: The Pythagorean Theorem Test, Part 1 [online]
This part of the Unit Test is online. It will be scored by the computer.

Unit Test: The Pythagorean Theorem Test, Part 2 [offline]
This part of the Unit Test is offline.

1. Complete each question on your own. Show all your work.

2. Submit this part to your Learning Coach for a grade.

Student Guide

Extended Problems: Real-World Application

Woodworking requires solid math skills for measuring and fitting pieces of wood together accurately. Many products include right angles, and for these, woodworkers use the Pythagorean theorem to solve challenging problems. Think about these woodworking problems:

- How can you ensure that a joint forms a right angle?
- How can you calculate a diagonal distance on a flat surface?
- How can you calculate diagonal distances in a rectangular box?

In this lesson, you'll complete Extended Problems: Real-World Application for the Pythagorean Theorem unit.

Goals for This Lesson
- Apply mathematical knowledge and skills to evaluate and analyze real-world situations.

Graded Activities in This Lesson
Extended Problems: Real-World Application

Extended Problems: Real-World Application [offline]
You will complete a graded assignment that focuses on a real-world application of math.

Your Learning Coach will score this assignment.

- **Complete** the assignment on your own.
- **Submit** the completed assignment to your Learning Coach.

Student Guide

Project Research 1

Every location in the world has its own climate, or typical weather pattern. Some locations may be hot and receive little precipitation, while others may be cool and receive a great deal of precipitation.

Climate affects many decisions in society. For instance, does your house or apartment building have a roof that retains heat or reflects heat? Does your city have a plan for snow removal or an alert system for tornadoes? Because climate can have major impacts, climatologists work hard to understand it.

Goals for This Lesson
- Conduct research to gather data about two variables.

Graded Activities in This Lesson
There is no graded activity associated with this lesson.

Materials
Project Overview
Project Template
Sample Project
Sample Scatter Plot

Optional
Intermediate Mathematics C: A Reference Guide and Problem Sets

Groundwork: Preparing for the Lesson [online]
You will learn about how geography and climate are associated. You will also learn how to create a linear model in a spreadsheet.

Explore: Research: Climate Statistics [offline]
First, review the Sample Project. Then in the Project Overview, locate the **Project Instructions** section.

- Follow the instructions in the **Template** section of the Project Overview.

- Follow the instructions in the **Project Research** section of the Project Overview.

Note: You have until the end of the Project Research 2 lesson to complete your research. It is recommended that you complete the first Research slide during this lesson.

Take notes as you research.

Project Overview

Climate Statistics

Review the instructions for completing the project. This project is worth 20 points.

Goals

Climate is an area's typical weather pattern, or conditions. Have you ever wondered what influences an area's climate? For instance, does an area's average elevation influence its average temperature? Does an area's latitude or longitude influence its average temperature or rainfall?

For this project, you will analyze climate and geography data for various cities of your choosing.

First you'll find the data. Then you'll construct and interpret a table, a scatter plot, and a linear model of the data. Finally, you'll reflect on your findings.

Schedule of Completion

Project Research: 2 days

Project Writing: 2 days

Project Reflection: 1 day

Project Instructions

Before you begin, review the Sample Project so that you understand what you'll be creating.

Template

Download the Project Template (in PowerPoint). Rename the file studentname_ClimateStatistics, replacing "studentname" with your last name followed by your first initial. This file will become your presentation.

Project Research

1. Choose 12 cities in the United States, each from a different state. Then, choose one climate feature and one geographic feature that you think might be associated with each other. You'll study those features for each city you chose. For instance, if you hypothesize that higher elevation is associated with greater or lesser rainfall, you might choose to study the average elevation of each city along with each city's average annual rainfall.

    -   Some features you can consider are average annual rainfall, average temperature, average elevation, and latitude and longitude. These are just a few suggestions. Feel free to explore other ideas.

    -   You may study the same features as those shown in the sample project (average annual rainfall vs. average elevation); however, you must collect data from different cities.

    -   *Tip:* It's likely that you will not be able to find all the information you need on one website. For example, you may have to search separately for average annual rainfall by city and for average elevation by city.

2. Open your presentation, and follow the directions to complete the Research slides.

    - On the first Research slide, fill in the tables with data from your websites.

    - Double-check that you typed all the data correctly.

    - On the Units of Measure slide, name your variables and describe the units of measure used for each of them. For instance, average rainfall by city may be measured in inches, and average elevation may be measured in feet.

Project Writing

1. Before you begin writing, complete the Practice Test, a computer-scored, ungraded assessment. You'll practice analyzing scatter plots and writing the equation for a linear model, skills essential to completing your project. Reach out to your teacher with any questions you have after taking this Practice Test.

2. Follow the directions in the presentation to complete each Writing slide.

    - To complete the Scatter Plot slide, you will need to use spreadsheet software to construct the scatter plot. If you're unsure about how to construct a scatter plot using your software, ask your teacher for assistance.

Project Reflection

Look back over the Writing slides in your presentation. Follow the directions in the presentation to complete the Reflection slide.

Submission

Confirm that your presentation contains all your work:

- Weather and geography data for 12 cities along with source information

- A scatter plot with a discussion of the graph

- A scatter plot with a linear model and a discussion of the linear model

- The computations for finding the equation for the linear model along with the final equation

- Your reflection.

Submit your presentation to your teacher.

Student Guide

Project Research 2

In this lesson, you'll complete the research for the Climate Statistics project.

Goals for This Lesson
- Conduct research to gather data about two variables.

Graded Activities in This Lesson
There is no graded activity associated with this lesson.

Materials
Project Overview
Project Template
Sample Project

Optional
Intermediate Mathematics C: A Reference Guide and Problem Sets

---

Explore: Research: Climate Statistics [offline]
Complete the following tasks, described in the **Project Instructions** section of the Project Overview:

- Review the **Sample Project**.

- Follow the instructions in the **Template** section of the Project Overview.

- Follow the instructions in the **Project Research** section of the Project Overview.

Take notes as you research.

Project Overview

Climate Statistics

Review the instructions for completing the project. This project is worth 20 points.

Goals

Climate is an area's typical weather pattern, or conditions. Have you ever wondered what influences an area's climate? For instance, does an area's average elevation influence its average temperature? Does an area's latitude or longitude influence its average temperature or rainfall?

For this project, you will analyze climate and geography data for various cities of your choosing.

First you'll find the data. Then you'll construct and interpret a table, a scatter plot, and a linear model of the data. Finally, you'll reflect on your findings.

Schedule of Completion

Project Research: 2 days

Project Writing: 2 days

Project Reflection: 1 day

Project Instructions

Before you begin, review the Sample Project so that you understand what you'll be creating.

Template

Download the Project Template (in PowerPoint). Rename the file studentname_ClimateStatistics, replacing "studentname" with your last name followed by your first initial. This file will become your presentation.

Project Research

1. Choose 12 cities in the United States, each from a different state. Then, choose one climate feature and one geographic feature that you think might be associated with each other. You'll study those features for each city you chose. For instance, if you hypothesize that higher elevation is associated with greater or lesser rainfall, you might choose to study the average elevation of each city along with each city's average annual rainfall.

   - Some features you can consider are average annual rainfall, average temperature, average elevation, and latitude and longitude. These are just a few suggestions. Feel free to explore other ideas.

   - You may study the same features as those shown in the sample project (average annual rainfall vs. average elevation); however, you must collect data from different cities.

   - *Tip:* It's likely that you will not be able to find all the information you need on one website. For example, you may have to search separately for average annual rainfall by city and for average elevation by city.

2. Open your presentation, and follow the directions to complete the Research slides.

- On the first Research slide, fill in the tables with data from your websites.

- Double-check that you typed all the data correctly.

- On the Units of Measure slide, name your variables and describe the units of measure used for each of them. For instance, average rainfall by city may be measured in inches, and average elevation may be measured in feet.

Project Writing

1. Before you begin writing, complete the Practice Test, a computer-scored, ungraded assessment. You'll practice analyzing scatter plots and writing the equation for a linear model, skills essential to completing your project. Reach out to your teacher with any questions you have after taking this Practice Test.

2. Follow the directions in the presentation to complete each Writing slide.

- To complete the Scatter Plot slide, you will need to use spreadsheet software to construct the scatter plot. If you're unsure about how to construct a scatter plot using your software, ask your teacher for assistance.

Project Reflection

Look back over the Writing slides in your presentation. Follow the directions in the presentation to complete the Reflection slide.

Submission

Confirm that your presentation contains all your work:

- Weather and geography data for 12 cities along with source information

- A scatter plot with a discussion of the graph

- A scatter plot with a linear model and a discussion of the linear model

- The computations for finding the equation for the linear model along with the final equation

- Your reflection.

Submit your presentation to your teacher.

Student Guide

Project Writing 1

In this lesson, you'll create and discuss a scatter plot of the data you collected in your research. Before you begin writing, you will take a Practice Test to show what you know, and to receive feedback, about analyzing scatter plots and writing an equation for a linear model.

Goals for This Lesson

- Create scatter plots from given data.

- Interpret scatter plots.

- Identify clusters and outliers in a scatter plot.

- Describe patterns in data.

- Use a linear model to approximate relationships between two quantitative variables.

- Present research in a written or oral format.

Graded Activities in This Lesson

There is no graded activity associated with this lesson.

Materials

Project Overview
Project Template
Sample Project
Sample Scatter Plot

Optional

Intermediate Mathematics C: A Reference Guide and Problem Sets

---

Explore: Writing: Climate Statistics [offline]

In this lesson, you'll begin writing. For specific guidance, go to the **Project Instructions** section in the Project Overview. Follow the instructions under **Project Writing**.

Note: You have until the end of the Project Writing 2 lesson to complete **Project Writing**. However, it is recommended that you complete the scatter plot and the scatter plot discussion in this lesson.

Practice Test: Scatter Plots and Linear Models [online]

Complete the Practice Test to review some math skills that you'll use as you write.

Student Guide

Project Writing 2

In this lesson, you'll complete the writing for the project.

Goals for This Lesson
- Create scatter plots from given data.

- Interpret scatter plots.

- Identify clusters and outliers in a scatter plot.

- Describe patterns in data.

- Use a linear model to approximate relationships between two quantitative variables.

- Present research in a written or oral format.

Graded Activities in This Lesson
There is no graded activity associated with this lesson.

Materials
Project Overview
Project Template
Sample Project

Optional
Intermediate Mathematics C: A Reference Guide and Problem Sets

Explore: Writing: Climate Statistics [offline]
Complete the tasks described in the **Project Instructions** section of the Project Overview.

- Review the **Sample Project**.

- Follow the instructions under Step 2 of **Project Writing**.

Student Guide

Project Reflection

You have researched geographic and climatic features of 12 different cities. Did you expect your data to have the association that your scatter plot showed? Are there any other factors that might have influenced your findings? If you had graphed the variables on opposite axes, would the graph have changed? Would the variables' association have changed?

In this lesson, you'll reflect on your project by answering questions like these about the scatter plot and the linear model that you created, and then you'll submit your completed presentation.

Goals for This Lesson

- Interpret scatter plots.

- Describe patterns in data.

- Interpret the slope as the rate for a linear model.

- Interpret the *y*-intercept as the initial value for a linear model.

- Present research in a written or oral format.

- Apply mathematical knowledge and skills to evaluate and analyze real-world situations.

Graded Activities in This Lesson

Project: Climate Statistics

Materials

Project Overview
Project Template
Sample Project

Optional

Intermediate Mathematics C: A Reference Guide and Problem Sets

---

Explore: Reflection: Climate Statistics [offline]

Go to the **Project Instructions** section in the Project Overview.

- Review the **Sample Project**.

- Follow the instructions under **Project Reflection**.

Use What You Know: Submit Your Presentation [online]

Go to the **Submission** section in the Project Overview. Check that you've completed all tasks listed in that section. Once you've confirmed that your presentation is complete, submit the completed assignment according to your teacher's instructions.

Student Guide

Semester Review

You have learned about direct linear variation, quadratic variation, scatter plots, and linear models. You've learned about basic geometric shapes, such as points, lines, planes, pairs of angles, parallel lines and transversals, triangles, and polygons. You've also learned about congruence and similarity and transformations.

You have learned how to identify and simplify rational and irrational numbers and how to solve equations involving square roots and cube roots. Finally, you learned how to use the Pythagorean theorem to solve problems involving right triangles.

Goals for This Lesson
- Review the concepts and skills learned in the semester.

Graded Activities in This Lesson
There is no graded activity associated with this lesson.

Materials
Intermediate Mathematics C: A Reference Guide and Problem Sets

Optional
calculator

Keywords
acute angle: an angle that measures less than 90°

acute triangle: a triangle with three acute angles

adjacent angles: two angles in the same plane that share a vertex and a side, but do not share any interior points

alternate exterior angles: the outside angles on opposite diagonal sides of a transversal crossing two parallel lines

alternate interior angles: the inside angles on opposite diagonal sides of a transversal crossing two parallel lines

angle: the figure formed by two rays, called sides, that share the same endpoint

base of a cylinder: one of the parallel, congruent faces of the cylinder; a base of a cylinder is a circle

bivariate data: data that show the relationship between two variables; paired data

categorical variable: a variable that is separable into mutually exclusive groups (for example, boys and girls, or athletes and nonathletes)

center of rotation: the point about which a figure is rotated

center of a sphere: the point to which all points on the surface of a sphere are equidistant

cluster: in a scatter plot, a group of points that are close together in comparison with the other points

complementary angles: a pair of angles for which the sum of their measures is 90°

concave polygon: a polygon in which at least one line segment that connects any two points inside the polygon does not lie completely inside the polygon

cone: a three-dimensional figure with one base that is a circle, a curved lateral surface, and a point called a vertex

congruent angles: angles that have equal measures

congruent polygons: polygons that are the same size and shape

congruent segments: segments that have equal lengths

converse: the statement that is formed when the "if" and "then" of an original statement are interchanged

convex polygon: a polygon in which every line segment connecting any two points inside the polygon lies completely inside the polygon

corresponding angles: the angles that lie in the same position or "match up" when a transversal crosses two parallel lines

cylinder: a three-dimensional figure with two congruent, parallel bases that are circles and a curved lateral surface that joins them

diagonal: a segment that connects two vertices of a polygon and does not lie along any side of the polygon

dilation: a transformation that changes the size, but not the shape, of a figure

direct variation: a function defined by an equation of the form $y = kx$, where k is a nonzero constant; when you use this equation, you can say that y varies directly as x

exterior angle of a polygon: an angle formed by two sides of a polygon, one of which extends outside the polygon; each interior angle of a polygon forms a linear pair with an exterior angle

frequency: the number of observations within a range of data

hypotenuse: the side opposite the right angle in a right triangle

image: in a transformation, the new figure that results from the transformation

initial amount: the beginning value of a linear relationship before any time has passed; the initial amount, also known as the initial value, is the y-intercept of the line

interior angle: any of the angles inside a polygon

irrational number: any real number that cannot be written in the form a/b for any integers a and b; in decimal form, all irrational numbers are nonterminating and nonrepeating; the set of irrational numbers is denoted by I

lateral face: a face that is not a base

lateral surface: the curved surface of a cylinder or cone; in a prism, any surface that connects the two bases; in a pyramid, any surface that rises from the base to the vertex

legs of a right triangle: the two sides forming the right angle

line: a collection of points arranged in a straight path

line of reflection: the line that a figure is reflected across

line segment: part of a line that includes any two points on the line and all the points in between the two points

linear association: in a scatter plot, the points follow a pattern that resembles a line

linear model: a line drawn to fit the trend of the points in a scatter plot

linear pair: two angles that have a common side and whose other sides point in opposite directions

mean (average): the sum of the values in a data set divided by the number of values

median: for a data set with an odd number of values, the middle value after the values have been ordered from least to greatest; for a data set with an even number of values, the mean of the two middle values after the values have been ordered from least to greatest

mode: the data value(s) occurring most often in a data set

negative association: an inverse relationship; as the value of one variable goes up, the value of the other variable tends to go down

no association: a lack of association between two variables on a scatter plot

nonlinear association: in a scatter plot, the points follow a pattern that does not resemble a line

obtuse angle: an angle that measures greater than 90° and less than 180°

obtuse triangle: a triangle with an obtuse angle

outlier: a data value in a data set that is either much smaller or much larger than the other data in the set

parallel lines: coplanar lines that never intersect

perfect square: a whole number whose square root is an integer

polygon: a closed figure formed by three or more line segments in a plane, such that each line segment intersects exactly two other line segments at their endpoints only

positive association: a direct relationship; as the value of one variable goes up, the value of the other variable tends to go up, too

pre-image: the original figure in a transformation

principal square root: the nonnegative square root, indicated by the square root sign

Pythagorean Theorem: in any right triangle, the square of the length of the hypotenuse equals the sum of the squares of the lengths of the legs

quadratic variation: a relationship between x and y in which you can write the function describing the relationship in a form of the general equation $y = kx^2$, where k is a nonzero constant

radius of a sphere: the distance from the center of a sphere to the sphere's surface

range: the largest number in a dataset minus the smallest number

rate of change: the rate at which quantities change over time in a linear relationship; the rate of change is the slope of the line

rational number: any number that can be expressed as a ratio (a/b), where a and b are integers and b is nonzero; the set of rational numbers is represented by Q

rational square root: a square root that is a rational number

reflection: a transformation of a figure by flipping it across a line or line segment, creating a mirror image of the figure

regular polygon: a polygon that is both equilateral and equiangular

relative frequency: the number of observations within a given class or category, divided by the total number of observations: $\dfrac{\# \text{ of observations within a class}}{\text{total } \# \text{ of observations}}$; if there is more than one class, each relative frequency will be less than 1, and all relative frequencies will add up to 1

right angle: an angle that measures 90°

right triangle: a triangle with a right angle

rotation: a transformation of a figure by turning it about a given point

scale factor: a ratio of one measure to another, where both measures are the same unit of measure

scatter plot: a graph that displays two-dimensional data as points; scatter-plot points represent ordered pairs

side (of a polygon): one of the line segments that form a polygon

similar figures: figures that have the same shape but not necessarily the same size

similar polygons: polygons that have the same shape, but not necessarily the same size

sphere: a figure in space made up of all points equidistant from a given point

square root: a factor of a number that when multiplied by itself results in the number; the nonnegative square root is called the principal square root and is indicated by the square root sign

straight angle: an angle that measures 180°

supplementary angles: a pair of angles for which the sum of their measures is 180°

theorem: a statement that is shown to be true by use of a logically developed argument

translation: the movement of a figure along a line, sometimes called a *slide*

transversal: a line that intersects two or more lines in a plane

two-way table: a table used to compare two categorical variables

vector: a line segment with a direction indicated with an arrow

vertex: a point common to two sides of an angle or polygon; the plural of vertex is vertices

vertical angles: a pair of nonadjacent angles formed by two intersecting lines

volume: the measure of the space inside (or the space occupied by) a three-dimensional figure

Semester Review: Look Back at the Semester [online]
You will review key concepts from the semester to prepare for the Semester Test.

Offline Learning: Prepare for the Semester Test [offline]
Complete the following problems:

- Problems 1–18 on pages 296–297

- Problems 1–14 on pages 336–337

- Problems 1–17 odd on pages 366–367

- Problems 1–5 and 6–14 even on pages 416–417

- Problems 1–7 and 9–25 odd on pages 452–453

- Problems 1–6 and 8–12 even on pages 480–481

Use the Topic Lookups to review topics for any problems that were difficult for you.

Student Guide

Semester Test, Part 1

It's time to take the Semester Test. This Semester Test has two parts—one part that will be scored by the computer and one part that your Learning Coach will score. You will complete the computer-scored part in this lesson.

Goals for This Lesson

- Find the constant of variation when given data for a function with direct linear variation.

- Solve a problem involving direct linear variation.

- Solve problems involving direct variation.

- Find the constant of variation when given data for a function with quadratic variation.

- Solve a problem involving quadratic variation.

- Write a formula for a problem involving a quadratic variation.

- Graph a function involving quadratic variation.

- Construct and interpret a two-way table summarizing data on two categorical variables collected from the same subjects.

- Use relative frequencies calculated for rows or columns to describe possible association between bivariate categorical data.

- Create scatter plots from given data.

- Interpret scatter plots.

- Identify clusters and outliers in a scatter plot.

- Describe patterns in data.

- Use a linear model to approximate relationships between two quantitative variables.

- Interpret the slope as the rate for a linear model.

- Interpret the *y*-intercept as the initial value for a linear model.

- Identify points, lines, or planes in a figure.

- Name points, lines, and planes.

- Identify a pair of alternate interior and alternate exterior angles associated with a transversal that intersects parallel lines.

- Identify a pair of corresponding angles associated with a transversal that intersects parallel lines.

- Use properties to determine unknown angle measures associated with a transversal that intersects two parallel lines.

- Use properties to determine unknown angle measures associated with a transversal that intersects two parallel lines in a complex figure.

- Identify linear pairs, vertical angles, and adjacent angles.

- Solve problems involving pairs of angles.

- Find measures of complements and/or supplements of angles.

- Use the triangle sum theorem to find a missing angle measure in a triangle.

- Determine whether a triangle is acute, obtuse, or right.

- Classify a polygon by the number of sides and determine if it is concave or convex.

- Determine the sum of the measures of the interior angles of a polygon given the number of sides, and vice versa.

- Classify a polygon by the number of sides and determine if it is concave or convex.

- Determine the sum of the measures of the interior angles of a polygon given the number of sides, and vice versa.

- Identify regular polygons and determine the measure of each interior angle.

- Use properties to determine unknown values associated with internal and external angles of a triangle.

- Find measures of segments and angles.

- Find the exact volume of a cylinder.

- Use an approximation for pi to estimate the volume of a cylinder.

- Solve problems involving the volume of a cylinder.

- Find the volume of a cone using pi or an approximation for pi.

- Solve problems involving the volume of a cone.

- Find the exact volume of a sphere.

- Find the approximate volume of a sphere.

- Solve problems involving the exact or approximate volume of a sphere.

- Solve problems involving volume of solid figures.

- Identify congruent and similar polygons.

- Use congruence to find missing side or angle measures.

- Use proportions to find missing side lengths for similar figures.

- Determine whether two figures are similar and find a missing side length in a pair of similar figures.

- Find the scale factor for a pair of similar figures with at least one known pair of corresponding sides.

- Determine whether a transformation is a reflection, a rotation, or a translation.

- Experimentally verify the properties of rotations, reflections, and translations.

- Describe a transformation using coordinates.

- Dilate a figure using a given scale factor.

- Find the scale factor of a dilation.

- Use transformations to determine if two figures are similar.

- Use the AA criterion to determine if two triangles are similar.

- Describe a transformation using a sequence of transformations.

- Order rational numbers.

- Express a fraction as a decimal.

- Find a rational number between two given rational numbers.

- Find a number that is between two rational numbers.

- Express a decimal as the ratio of two integers.

- Classify a number as rational or irrational.

- Find square roots of a perfect square.

- Solve a simple equation with squares.

- Approximate a square root to the nearest tenth.

- Write the square root of a positive whole number in simplified radical form.

- Solve a word problem involving square roots.

- Solve an equation that involves a rational square root.

- Solve an equation that involves an irrational square root.

- Solve an equation that involves a cube root.

- Approximate irrational square roots.

- Use the Pythagorean Theorem to find a missing length in a right triangle.

- Use the converse of the Pythagorean Theorem to determine whether a triangle with given side lengths is a right triangle.

- Explain a proof of the Pythagorean theorem and its converse.

- Use the Pythagorean Theorem to solve a word problem.

- Solve a word problem involving right triangles.

- Use the Pythagorean theorem to find diagonal distances in the coordinate plane.

- Use the Pythagorean theorem to find distances in 3-dimensional objects.

- Use the Pythagorean theorem to solve area problems.

- Use models to show the Pythagorean theorem.

- Use the Pythagorean theorem to solve problems involving 3-dimensional objects.

Graded Activities in This Lesson
Semester Test: Intermediate Mathematics C, Part 1

Semester Test: Intermediate Mathematics C, Part 1 [online]
You will complete a test covering the main goals of this semester. This part of the test is online. It will be scored by the computer.

Student Guide

Semester Test, Part 2

It's time to take the offline part of the Semester Test.

Goals for This Lesson

- Interpret scatter plots.

- Describe patterns in data.

- Use a linear model to approximate relationships between two quantitative variables.

- Interpret the slope as the rate for a linear model.

- Interpret the *y*-intercept as the initial value for a linear model.

- Classify a polygon by the number of sides and determine if it is concave or convex.

- Determine the sum of the measures of the interior angles of a polygon given the number of sides, and vice versa.

- Use an approximation for pi to estimate the volume of a cylinder.

- Solve problems involving the volume of a cylinder.

- Find the volume of a cone using pi or an approximation for pi.

- Solve problems involving the volume of a cone.

- Find the approximate volume of a sphere.

- Solve problems involving the exact or approximate volume of a sphere.

- Solve problems involving volume of solid figures.

- Express a decimal as the ratio of two integers.

- Write the square root of a positive whole number in simplified radical form.

- Approximate a square root to the nearest tenth.

- Use the Pythagorean theorem to find diagonal distances in the coordinate plane.

Graded Activities in This Lesson

Semester Test: Intermediate Mathematics C, Part 2

Semester Test: Intermediate Mathematics C, Part 2 [offline]

This part of the Semester Test is offline.

1. Complete each question on your own. Show all your work.

2. Submit this part to your Learning Coach for a grade.